Relaxation
Scripts
for
Harmony,
Tranquility,
Serenity

Relaxation Scripts *for* Harmony, Tranquility, Serenity

Edited by
Donald A Tubesing
&
Nancy Loving Tubesing

WHOLE PERSON ASSOCIATES
Duluth, Minnesota

Whole Person Associates
210 West Michigan
Duluth, MN 55802-1908
800-247-6789

Relaxation Scripts for Harmony, Tranquility, Serenity

Printed in the United States of America
10 9 8 7 6 5 4 3 2 1

ISBN 1-57025-212-2

The relaxation scripts in this book were selected from the 360 activities in Whole Person Associates *Structured Exercises in Stress Management* and *Structured Exercises in Wellness Promotion*. We are grateful to the contributors who so generously shared their creative work.

Many of the scripts (see notes at the end of each script) are available on CD and audiotape.

Call 800-247-6789 for a catalog or visit our Web site, www.wholeperson.com.

Contents

Introduction

You may be an old hand at teaching people about relaxation and are looking for new ideas. Or perhaps you're a beginner, just testing the water. Whatever your needs, the scripts in this book provide a whole family of techniques for reducing physical and mental stress. To assist you in selecting the right script for your audience, we offer a brief introduction to the theory behind different types of relaxation.

Deep Breathing
Deep, rhythmic breathing is the easiest and most reliable way to begin relaxing. Whenever you breathe in or hold your breath, you increase tension in your body. As you breathe out, your body automatically releases tension, and in the pause before you inhale, relaxes naturally. Deep breathing is the primary building block for all other relaxation techniques, including the three classic relaxation forms: progressive muscle relaxation, autogenic relaxation, and meditation.

Progressive
Probably the most familiar relaxation format in the United States, this technique was developed in the 1920s by Dr. Edmund Jacobson and is based on a simple principle you've probably noticed yourself: when you tense a muscle and then let go, the muscle relaxes more deeply after the release. Progressive muscle relaxation is a clinically-proven technique for controlling muscle tension and producing profound relaxation by systematically tensing and then relaxing the major

muscle groups. The Unwinding script in the Relaxation Classics section of this book teaches progressive relaxation.

Autogenic Relaxation

First introduced in 1932 by Drs. Johanes Schultz and Wolfgange Luthe, autogenic techniques teach the stressed mind and body to relax quickly on verbal command and to return from an "alarm" state to a balanced, normal state. Autogenic routines combine deep, rhythmic breathing with images of draining or melting tension away rather than tightening and relaxing muscles. They often use imagery of warmth and heaviness to enhance sensations and promote circulation. The Warm script in the Relaxation Classics section of this book teaches autogenic relaxation.

Meditation

Meditation has been practiced by people in religious contexts for 5,000 years. Dr. Herbert Benson was responsible for identifying the relaxation benefits of meditative states and incorporating them into an effective secular technique he called the "Relaxation Response." Like autogenic strategies, meditation begins with a quiet environment, a passive uncritical attitude, and a rhythmic breathing cadence. But the object in meditation is to clear the mind and then concentrate on a single mental focus (sound, image, object, or phrase) for an extended period of time.

Guided Imagery and Visualization

Imaging is an easy, natural process you use hundreds of times a day — any time you visualize the face of a loved one, mentally hum a favorite tune, or recall and anticipate the taste of a special food. The same valuable process can help you relax when you're in a tough spot or after a busy day. The visualizations in this book combine imagery, sensory awareness, and deep breathing in relaxing mental journeys to imaginary places of peace, comfort, healing, empowerment, and revitalization.

Stretching Routines

Stretching is a natural stress reliever that encourages flexibility, reduces tension, and releases trapped energy. When you stretch, the fibers of your muscles separate, allowing more blood to revitalize each muscle cell. For maximum benefit, concentrate on the muscles in which you feel stress — most likely your back and neck. Stretch gently and hold, but never to the point of discomfort.

Massage for Tension Relief

Massage harnesses the healing, revitalizing power of touch. The gentle rubbing of forehead, face, and head at your desk; a deep-muscle, full-body manipulation at the health club, or stimulation of acupressure points by a trained massage therapist are all excellent ways to help tense muscles let go and relax.

Before You Begin

You can teach relaxation in any setting, but if it's available, a quiet room with comfortable seating or floor mats and light that can be dimmed will make it easier for people tune out distractions and tune in to their own sensations and imagination.

Quiet background music helps set a mood and masks sounds from outside the room. Choose music that has flowing melodies and is generally low pitched. Instrumental music from Steven Halpern and Steven Eckels is available from Whole Person Associates. Whether you use CDs or audiotapes, have them cued up and ready to go with the volume set appropriately.

Keep the music soft so you can be heard easily as you speak in a calm, quiet manner. Pacing is important. You should read the scripts slowly, not by elongating every word, but by pausing between phrases and sentences for people to visualize a scene or follow your instructions. If you ask people to make a fist and then release it, watch them do so and don't move on until their hands are open and relaxed.

As the session draws to an end, gradually increase the volume of your voice and the speed of your presentation to help people return comfortably to full alertness.

Relaxation Classics

*B*ody Scan

This self-awareness interlude teaches participants a technique for attending to tense spots in the body — becoming aware of them and releasing the tension.

Time
2–3 minutes

Describe the goals of body scanning to participants and then ask them to get into a comfortable position and take five slow, deep breaths.

&&&

I'm going to take you on an imaginary trip through your body...

On this journey through your own insides you will search for tension... Please pay close attention to any tension you detect and its specific location...

When you discover a tense area, you may want to exaggerate it slightly so you can become even more aware of the tension...

Say to yourself, I'm tensing my neck muscles... I'm

tightening my back... I'm holding my shoulders... I'm aching my stomach... I'm hurting myself...

Again, notice the tension you're holding... and then let go, allowing the tension to drain away...

Take your time as you focus on each body part...

Periodically ask yourself, "Where am I tense?"

Follow me through your body now in search of lurking tension.

Begin by focusing your attention on your toes... simply notice them and how they feel...

Don't rush! Allow sufficient time at each body region for people to focus on the tension they discover. If you participate in the process, your body should give you clues to appropriate pacing.

Move slowly up your body...

Move your attention to your feet... heels... ankles... shins... calves... knees... thighs... buttocks... hips... genital area... abdomen... stomach... chest... back... shoulders... neck... head... face... forehead... arms... elbows... forearms... wrists... hands... fingertips...

Begin now to prepare yourself to come back into this room...

But before you return, quickly scan your body once more and recall exactly where and in what form you found tension...

Adapted from *Structured Exercises in Wellness Promotion, vol. 2,* also available on the *Natural Tranquilizers* CD and audiotape.

*U*nwinding

Participants experience a state of profound relaxation as they explore the stress/relaxation connection in this revitalizing skill-builder.

Time
20–30 minutes

Introduce the exercise by explaining that this exercise will help participants learn the skill of deep relaxation, which is so important for stress reduction, stress management, and overall health and well-being.

&&&

Get comfortable now... find a relaxed position and allow yourself to concentrate fully on these instructions...

Take a deep breath in through your nose... and as you let it out through your mouth... allow your eyes to close slowly and comfortably...

Let your body begin to relax and unwind... Take another deep breath... and as you exhale let it carry all the tension out of your body... Allow a feeling of peacefulness to descend over you... a pleasant and enjoyable sensation of being comfortable and at ease...

Now turn your attention to your body and begin to pay close attention to the sensations you experience...notice the signals your body is sending you...

Find the place in your body that seems most tense... and allow that muscle to let go of its hold...Begin to let all your muscles...all over your body...give up their hold and go limp...Now is the time to let go of whatever tension you have been holding on to...

Focus again on your breathing...filling yourself up as you breathe in...and letting that tension go when you breathe out...

Now direct your attention to the top of your head... and allow a feeling of relaxation to begin there...Let that feeling of relaxation spread downward through your body...

Let the small muscles of your scalp relax...and now allow all the muscles of your forehead to relax and let go ...Pay special attention to your forehead...let yourself really feel the muscle there giving up its hold...Feel your eyebrows sagging down...Let all the muscles around the sides and back of your head relax fully and completely...Imagine that your ears are drooping under their own weight... Now allow your cheek and face muscles to relax and let go...let your jaw muscles relax...and allow your jaw to drop slightly...Allow the muscles of your lips and chin to relax and grow limp.

Now all the muscles of your head and face have let go... and are smooth and relaxed...

Next, let the muscles of your neck relax slightly...
tensing them only enough to hold your head upright
and balanced easily in position... Let the feeling of
relaxation spread into your throat... and down the sides
of your neck... into your shoulders... Allow your
shoulders to become heavy and sag downward... as you
relax all your neck and throat and shoulder muscles...

Now, allow the feeling of relaxation you're experiencing
to spread downward to the muscles of your chest and
upper back... Feel the relaxation there as the muscles
release their hold... Feel the relaxation... Now, let your
shoulder muscles go completely limp... and allow your
arms to rest heavily... with your hands in your lap or on
your thighs... Feel your arms growing very heavy... and
relax all the muscles of your forearms, hands and
fingers... Let the tension flow right out your
fingertips... You are feeling very calm... and relaxed...
and comfortable throughout your upper body...

Notice your breathing for a few seconds ... notice how
regular it has become... Let that feeling of deep
relaxation spread fully through your chest... down
through the muscles of your back... and down into
your arms...

As you do so... allow your stomach muscles to relax
completely and totally... Your stomach will probably sag
just a bit as the muscles release their hold ... Allow that
sagging to occur and relax the muscles of your sides...
the muscles of your shoulder blades... and the small of
your back... Let all the muscles of your spine relax ...
let go all the way from your skull down to the tip of
your spine... Simply allow all of the muscles of your

stomach and sides and back to experience a sensation of warmth...and heaviness...relaxing more and more deeply...

Now, relax the large muscles of your thighs...and let them go completely limp...feel all your muscles so relaxed that they feel as though they're turning to jelly...Your whole body is becoming profoundly relaxed...Feel that relaxation now and enjoy it...Now, focus on the muscles of your buttocks...and let that relaxation spread into the front of your lower legs...into your shin muscles...into your ankles...allowing your ankles to feel free and loose...Now, wiggle your toes once or twice...and let all of the muscles of your feet give up their hold completely...Your whole body is extremely relaxed and comfortable...

Simply enjoy these sensations of profound relaxation throughout your body...notice that you can feel even more relaxed as you become aware of the warmth in your arms and hands...Feel this warmth and allow it to increase...Allow your arms to feel extremely heavy and completely limp...feel this growing sensation of warmth spreading way out to your fingertips...

Concentrate closely on your hands and your arms...and allow the feeling of pleasant heaviness and warmth to increase by itself...Simply observe the process and encourage it...Now allow those same feelings of heaviness and warmth to spread throughout your legs... Concentrate closely on the sensations in your legs...and let them become very, very heavy...very heavy and very warm...Your arms and legs are so heavy and so warm... Your entire body now is profoundly relaxed...and you

feel only a pleasant overall sensation of heaviness...
warmth and peace...

Now, I'd like you to turn your attention to your
breathing...and without interfering with your
breathing in any way...simply observe it...feel the
slow, peaceful rise and fall of your stomach as your
breath flows slowly in...and slowly out of your body...
Don't try to hurry your breathing or slow it down...Just
notice your breathing...and observe its slow, steady
process...Imagine that you've just discovered the steady
rising and falling of your stomach...and that you're
observing it with curiosity and respect...Wait patiently
for each breath to arrive...and notice its passing...
Notice, too, the brief periods of quiet after one breath
passes and before the next one arrives...

Now, continue to observe this breathing process and
begin to count your breaths as they arrive...As the first
one comes, watch it closely and hear yourself mentally
say, "one"...Wait patiently for the next one and count,
"two"...Continue until you've counted 25 breaths...
not allowing any other thoughts to distract you...

Pause here long enough to count 25 or 30 of your own
breaths and then gently continue the narration, allowing
your voice to get progressively stronger and more definite.

Now you're deeply relaxed...and you can return to this
peaceful state whenever you want to...Take a few
moments now to pay close attention to this relaxed
feeling...all over your body...and memorize it as
carefully as you can...Store the entire feeling of your
whole body in your memory...so that later you can

retrieve it and relax yourself at will...

When you feel ready to direct your awareness outside... and return to this place...allow yourself the time you need to wake up your body...and to bring it back to its usual level of alertness and responsiveness...

Wiggle your fingers and toes...your arms and legs a little bit...your shoulders...turn your head...but keep your eyes closed for a few seconds longer...as you experience all parts of your body reawakening...

Then, when you are ready, take a nice deep breath... open your eyes...and allow your body to feel fully alive and flowing with plenty of energy.

Adapted from *Structured Exercises in Stress Management, vol. 1,* available on the CD and audiotape *Relax... Let Go... Relax.*

I Am Relaxed

Adding the phrase "I am Relaxed" to a simple slow breathing technique partners mind and body to encourage deep relaxation.

Time
10–15 minutes

Materials
Optional: Large clock

&·&·&

Find a comfortable, relaxed posture with your body balanced and arms supported... Close your eyes and breathe slowly in and out... Enjoy the pleasure of feeling yourself breathe...

As you breathe in... mentally hear the words "I am"... As you breathe out... say to yourself, "relaxed"...

Try that for yourself... Tell yourself "I am" as you slowly breathe in... and say "relaxed" as you slowly exhale...

Continue to breathe like this for the next 10 minutes... focusing on your breathing and the words, "I am...

relaxed"...

Count your breaths on your fingers as you go... The best pacing will be about 40 breaths in 10 minutes... This is much slower than the average pace of 12–18 breaths per minute that we are accustomed to... so after 10 breaths you may want to open your eyes... look at the clock... and see if you can adjust your pace to about 4 breaths per minute...

Don't get preoccupied or worried about your timing... Just focus on your breathing... relax... and enjoy the process...

If you lose track counting... just start over again, focusing on breathing slowly and saying "I am... relaxed"... on each breath. If any other thoughts come to your mind... simply let these distractions pass right through and return your attention to your slow breathing and counting...

Take a deep breath and say "I am"... then exhale saying "relaxed"... and keep that slow, steady rhythm in your breathing... I'll let you know when it's time to stop...

Adapted from *Structured Exercises in Stress Management, vol. 4.*

Breathing for Relaxation

*T*en-Second Break

This ten-second breathing and auto-suggestion break will interrupt or prevent tension build-up and is ideal for instant stress relief. Try it whenever you feel irritated by small annoyances. It can also offer "breathing room" in conflict situations.

Time
5 minutes to learn, 10 seconds to use

&·&·&

Basic Routine
Smile as you think to yourself: My body doesn't need this irritation or stress.

Take a slow, deep belly breath...

Count to four slowly on the inhale and again on the exhale...

Take a second deep belly breath...closing your eyes at the top of the inhalation.

As you exhale ... imagine (visualize or feel) something warm entering your body at your head...and flowing

down into your hands and feet... Heaviness and warmth
are flowing in...

Think the phrase, "I am calm."

Open your eyes.

Modified Routine for Phone Calls
When the phone begins to ring, take a deep belly
breath . . . closing your eyes at the top of the inhalation.

As you exhale . . . imagine (visualize or feel) something
warm entering your body at your head... and flowing
down into your hands and feet... Heaviness and warmth
are flowing in...

Think the phrase, "I am calm."

Then answer the phone.

During the phone call, relax your shoulders and jaw.

Breathe from your abdomen as rhythmically as possible.

After the phone call: Do the complete Ten-Second
Break.

Adapted from *Structured Exercises in Stress Management, vol. 2.*

Complete Breath

Easy stretching postures build strength and resiliency, increase flexibility of joints and muscles, and promote physical and mental resiliency. The mental attitudes and breathing routines of Yoga are naturally calming and enhance concentration.

Yoga is best taught by a certified instructor, but if you're not an expert, don't be afraid to introduce your groups to the basic concepts, breathing techniques, and postures. Many groups will have experienced Yoga practitioners in their midst. Why not ask for knowledgeable participants to aid in your demonstration and teaching.

Time
Gear the length and depth of your presentation to the interest level and physical flexibility of your audience.

Begin by outlining the philosophy of Yoga and its health benefits.

The philosophy and mind/mind/spirit techniques of Yoga originated in India thousands of years ago, and the basic principles were outlined by the sage Patamjali over 2,000 years ago.

Yoga is essentially a quest for spiritual realization involving adherence to moral principles (non-violence, truthfulness, chastity, charity); purification of self through diet, self-discipline and study; postures; breathing techniques; emptying of the mind through disconnection from inner and outer senses; deep concentration; meditation; and the supreme state of the soul.

Yoga practices are based on the philosophy that for a contented life, you need a harmonious balance between your body, soul, and mind. It's tough to maintain a healthy equilibrium when we're under stress.

The breathing techniques (pranayama) and postures (asanas) of Yoga can be effective skills for stress management, even if you are not interested in the ethical, dietary, or meditative components of the philosophy.

The easy stretching postures build strength and resiliency, increase flexibility of joints and muscles, and promote physical and mental resiliency. The mental attitudes and breathing routines of Yoga are naturally calming and enhance concentration.

Yoga is a stress management techniques for all ages. It's safe and aesthetically pleasing to do. Research has demonstrated that practice of Yoga can produce additional powerful health benefits such as:

    & combatting stress and stress-related illness

    & lowering blood pressure

    & alleviating rheumatism and arthritis

    & reducing back problems

   & relieving migraine headaches

   & reducing fatigue

Invite participants to experience the relaxing effects of the Yoga breathing technique called the Complete Breath of Pranayana.

In Yoga the breath or prana is considered the life-force. Yoga believes that the more complete and rhythmic your breathing is, the more life force you will have available.

The Complete Breath in Yoga is very slow and quiet. Rhythm and flow are most important. The Complete Breath happens in three stages: abdomen, chest and shoulders. All breathing is done through the nose.

&*&*&

Sit as comfortably as possible, with your spine erect and your head balanced.

Place your feet solidly on the floor, legs slightly parted.

Allow your palms to rest comfortably on your thighs.

Start by tightening your abdomen muscles, noticing the control you have over their expansion and contraction...

Experiment with pushing your abdomen out as far as you can... and then contracting these muscles tighter, sucking in your gut...

Practice these distensions and contractions a few times.

Pause

Now begin a slow exhalation through your nose.

Simultaneously contract your abdomen until your lungs are completely empty...

Then begin a very slow inhalation and simultaneously push out your abdomen so the incoming air can get all the way to the bottom of your lungs...

Continuing your slow inhalation, contract your abdomen slightly while you expand your chest as much as possible...

Continuing to inhale slowly, raise your shoulders as high as possible, letting the air enter the top area of your lungs...

Hold on to your breath with your shoulders raised for a count of five: 1 – 2 – 3 – 4 – 5.

Now very slowly exhale...

As the breath flows ever so slowly out through your nose, allow your body to relax...

Contract your abdomen again at the end of the exhale, and without pause, repeat the breath...

Inhale... belly out... chest out... shoulders up...

Hold for a count of five: 1 – 2 – 3 – 4 –5.

Slowly relax and exhale...

Then contract your abdomen and repeat this breath three more times...

Remind participants to concentrate on allowing the movements to flow into each other and present the following introduction to the postures of Yoga:

Remember to keep breathing throughout as you assume the postures of Yoga. Don't hold your breath—keep the flow going.

Pay attention to the feedback from your body. Modify the pose so you can assume it with steadiness and ease.

Yoga is not a contest. More is not better. Do not hold any posture longer than the recommended time. Be sure to stop if you feel any strain or shaking.

Continue the complete breath technique as you assume the basic relaxation posture of Yoga called Savasana.

&&&

Find a place to sit on the floor. Give yourself enough space around you so that you will be able to stretch out on your back later.

As participants are finding their spots, distribute folded towels. It helps if you start with everyone facing the same direction.

Remember to keep breathing in your flowing rhythm.

Stretch your legs out in front of you and put your towel behind you, about where your head will be when you're fully stretched.

Now lean back on your elbows, keeping your trunk and legs in line.

Now lower your shoulders, head, and neck, adjusting the towel so your head is resting comfortably extended.

Now stretch and extend your toes and legs, then let them

relax. Allow your legs to roll naturally out to the side.

Stretch and extend your hands and arms, then let them relax comfortably at your sides, turning your palms up.

Allow yourself to relax as much as possible in this posture for 5 minutes, focusing on the flow of your breath.

Remind the group to relax rather than to strain to achieve and hold this posture.

After 5 minutes, gently interrupt and invite participants to come out of their relaxation slowly.

Imagine fresh energy entering every part of your body, starting at the head and moving down to the tips of your fingers and toes.

When you are fully revitalized, slowly sit up.

In closing, note that there are many Yoga postures and sequences that have different goals and benefits and then review the basic guidelines for using Yoga and encourage participants to seek additional training.

Make sure your space for Yoga is quiet, warm, and free from distraction.

Wear loose, comfortable clothes and make sure the floor surface is comfortable and not slippery.

Practice regularly for 15–30 minutes a day.

Always do Yoga on an empty stomach—just before a meal or two hours after eating.

Take a break. Rest periods between groups of postures complement the beneficial effects of the stretches. Stop for 3–5 minutes and let the tension flow out and the vitality flow in with your breath.

Find a qualified teacher and learn more about the various Yoga postures and sequences that have different goals and benefits.

Adapted from *Structured Exercises in Stress Management, vol. 5,* available on the CD and audiotape *Yoga.*

*T*ake a Deep Breath

Many people complain that they don't know how to relax or can't afford to waste time relaxing. This deceptively simple exercise teaches a five-minute routine that everyone can use anytime and anywhere to reduce body tension. Relaxation can easily be integrated into our daily lives if we just stop and breathe.

Time
10 minutes to learn, 5 minutes to use.

The best posture for deep breathing is lying on a firm surface with knees flexed, feet flat and slightly apart. If the meeting room furnishings preclude this pose, participants can sit comfortably in their chairs, with feet flat and arms supported as much as possible. Backs should be straight but not rigid.

&&&

Close your eyes and get as comfortable as possible...

Put one of your hands flat on your chest, and one hand on your abdomen between your navel and your breastbone. Take a deep breath, noticing the movement of your hands as you inhale and exhale...

This time I'd like you to breathe in slowly and deeply through your nose, bringing your breath all the way down into your belly so that it pushes up your hand as much as feels comfortable. Your chest should move only slightly and only as your belly rises...

Continue this slow deep breathing in through your nose and down into your belly... then gently let your breath go out again at a pace that's comfortable for you...

Pause here for a minute or so, allowing everyone to find a comfortable rhythm. If anyone seems to be having trouble, repeat the last paragraph once or twice before moving on.

Now I'd like you to smile slightly... relaxing your face muscles, while keeping up your own rhythm of breathing...

On the next breath, inhale deeply through your nose as before, and this time exhale through your mouth... making a soft and gentle "whooshing" sound, like wind in the pines or the ocean surf, as you blow out...

Let your mouth, tongue, jaw, and throat relax as you continue to take long slow breaths in through your nose... deep into your belly... and let them out through your mouth with a soft whooshing sound...

Focus on the sound and feeling of your breathing... as your belly rises and lowers and you become more and more relaxed.

Pause here for 3–4 minutes. If necessary, repeat the last two phrases once or twice during that time to keep the group inhaling deeply and exhaling noisily.

Compare the tension you feel now with the tension you experienced at the beginning of the exercise…and when you feel ready, open your eyes and bring your attention back to this room.

Encourage participants to practice deep breathing five minutes, twice a day for a week or two, focusing on the movement of the belly, the feeling of air flowing in and out, and the comfortable sense of relaxation.

Submitted by Ruth Strom-McCutcheon

Adapted from *Structured Exercises in Wellness Promotion, vol. 2,* available on the CD and audiotape *Take a Deep Breath.*

*C*leansing Breath

The goal of Yoga is a peaceful, clear mind in a sound, healthy body. Hatha Yoga approaches this goal from the physical aspect — through body postures, breathing techniques, diet, and deep relaxation.

The Cleansing Breath, or alternate nostril breathing, calms and balances the nervous system while promoting mental focus and relaxation. This technique is an excellent instant natural tranquilizer.

Time
5 minutes

To avoid confusion during the script, you may want to begin by demonstrating the technique, showing the proper hand position for closing alternate nostrils. Participants should remove their eyeglasses.

&&&

Sit up very tall, allowing your spine to lengthen and your shoulders to drop into a relaxed, but balanced posture...

Breathe slowly and gently through your nose...

feeling your chest and abdomen expanding with your
breath...

Then empty the air very slowly out of your nose
again...feeling your chest and your stomach relax...

Keep breathing deeply and gently through your nose...
down into your chest and abdomen...
then out through your nose...
relaxing your chest and stomach...

Continue to breathe deeply and gently...
while you bring your right hand up to your nose...

Rest the tips of your first two fingers on your
forehead...between your eyebrows...

Let your thumb rest gently on one side of your nose...
while your ring finger and pinky finger rest gently
against the other side of your nose...

Keep the same steady rhythm to your breathing...
on the next inhale, close your right nostril by pressing
gently with your thumb...

Inhale through the left nostril...
and then close off your left nostril with your ring
finger...
Hold for a count of four...
Now release your thumb and slowly exhale through the
right nostril to a count of 8 . . .

And then inhale again through your right nostril to a
count of 8...
Close both nostrils and hold to a count of 4...

Then release your ring finger
and exhale through your left nostril to a count of 8 ...

*Repeat this alternating pattern for ten breaths, maintaining
the 8–4–8 count beat and changing sides before each
exhale.*

Adapted from *Structured Exercises in Stress Management, vol. 5,*
available on the CD and audiotape *Yoga.*

Breath Prayer

Breathing opens us to the spiritual dimension of our being.
Tap into your inner healing resources and identify and
affirm core truths in this relaxing, rhythmic meditation.

Time
5–10 minutes, depending on whether you present the
script as written or invite participants to select their own
affirmation.

*Introduce the concept of a breath prayer affirmation by
reading the following information, continuing with the
brainstorming activity as time allows.*

A breath prayer is a repeated mental review of a meaningful phrase. The phrase could be a brief affirmation of
oneself, a statement of an eternal truth, a petition, an
image of a desired attitude, a proclamation of personal
commitment, an aspiration, or a goal.

The breath prayer phrase should easily divide in half for
inhalation and exhalation, so you can mentally say the
affirmation in rhythm with your breathing.

Take a few minutes now to brainstorm breath prayer
affirmations that are meaningful to you.

Provide examples such as those that follow if participants seem to need help:

I am... At peace
I am filled... With love
I am... Alive
I forgive... Myself
I am... Healing
I am... Renewed
Be still... Know God
Heal... Me

Ask participants to share the breath prayer phrases they listed. Invite them to choose a personal affirmation from their own list or an appealing idea suggested by others and then read the script.

&&&

Settle back comfortably now and begin to tune in to your body...
Stretch any part of your body that feels tight or tense...
Stretching and releasing...
Allowing any tension or tightness to free itself with the gentle movements of your stretch...

Close your eyes now...
Begin to tune out the noise and distractions of your environment...
Prepare to tune in to your inner silence...

Allow your focus to shift now to your breathing...
Pay attention to the easy, steady flow of your breath...
in and out... in and out...

as you breathe slowly and deeply...
listening to the quiet of your life-giving breath...

Pause 10 seconds.

As you continue to breathe with slow, full breaths...
begin to focus on the phrase I am calm...
hearing in your mind I am as you inhale...
and as you exhale . . . mentally hearing calm...
I am as you inhale...
calm as you exhale...
Continue to hear this affirmation as you inhale and
exhale ten times...

*Pause 45–50 seconds, gauging by your own ten deep
breaths.*

And now allow your own breath prayer to come into
your mind...
It may be the phrase you chose earlier...
or a new affirming prayer may come to you...
or you may continue with the I am...calm...

On your next inhalation...allow your healing phrase to
come to mind...
and continue for ten breaths or more...
praying in rhythm with your own breathing...

Pause one minute.

Now let your mental voice grow softer and softer...
as your attention shifts once again to the present time
and this place...
bringing back with you the relaxation...peace...and
healing...you have experienced...

As you inhale . . . stretch your hands and your feet...
Begin to become aware of the environment around
you...
Tune in to the sounds...
Become aware of the other people nearby...
Yet stay in touch with your profound sense of peace and
centeredness...

Pause 10 seconds.

When you are ready...open your eyes...and rejoin the
group...bringing with you the spirit of truth you have
rediscovered.

Adapted from *Structured Exercises in Stress Management, vol. 5,*
available on the CD and audiotape *Stress Escapes.*

Humming Breath

Participants enjoy a relaxing internal massage as they practice a mystical, musical Yoga technique for reducing tension.

Time
3–5 minutes

Provide a brief introduction to the value of humming as a stress reliever.

One of the simplest body/mind/spirit techniques for stress relief is one of the most ancient ones as well, dating back to ancient yoga practices—humming.

Focusing on the humming breath clears the mind, slows down and deepens breathing, and leads to a relaxing, meditative state.

Humming helps us tap into the healing power of music, while at the same time providing a delightful internal massage for the breathing passageways, relaxing these muscles through vibration.

Humming as a group reinforces a sense of connectedness

to our neighbors and oneness with all creation.

Invite participants to demonstrate their humming ability by humming a tune together.

Identify the person whose birthday is closest to today and hum Happy Birthday. Or choose another familiar tune that fits your audience or the time of year. Encourage people to hum loudly, not to worry about being in tune.

When everyone is warmed up to humming, direct participants to try a spontaneous one-note hum.

On the count of three, start humming your own personal hum.

The pitch and the volume don't matter, just find your own note and hum it.

I'll count to three and then begin humming. Keep on huming for 15–30 seconds, taking a breath when you need one...1...2...3...

After 30 seconds, begin leading the group through the yoga breath and humming sequence.

&·&·&

Close your eyes and relax as much as possible...

Take several deep breaths...

Breathe in easily through your nose...

As you breathe out, extend your breath fully, emptying your lungs completely...

With each succeeding breath, extend your exhale a little further and longer...

Allow time for at least three deep breaths...

On the next breath, close your lips and make a long, *high* humming sound as you exhale...

Help the group get started by humming yourself. Each hum can be repeated three times, or you can do one breath for each hum and then repeat the sequence.

On the next breath, exhale with a long *low* humming sound...

On the next breath, exhale with a *very loud* humming sound...

On the next breath, exhale with a *soft and sweet* humming sound...

On the next breath, exhale *without any sound*, and listen to the silence...

Inspiration for this technique came from Kenneth K Cohen's delightful yoga picture book for children, Imagine That! *(Santa Barbara CA: Santa Barbara Books, 1983)*

Adapted from *Structured Exercises in Stress Management, vol. 1,* available on the CD and audiotape *Yoga.*

$\int$ igh of Relief

This quick energizer provides an expressive relaxation break. Participants increase their repertoire of instant stress relievers as they release accumulated tension.

Time
3–5 minutes

Invite participants to join in an amusing experiment with tension relief.

&&&

Imagine for a moment that you've been under a lot of pressure or have been in a dangerous or frightening situation and suddenly the pressure is off, the danger is over.

Now would you please give a big sigh of relief, a "whew!" that says you're glad this close call or tough time is past.

If the group isn't responsive right away, exaggerate your own and goad them into action (eg, "Come on now, you don't sound very relieved—let me hear a big WHEW!"). Try getting two or three big sighs before moving on. Sometimes it helps if people stand up.

Then use a similar format to lead the group through three more tension-relieving sighs.

Let's try a sigh of disappointment:
OOOOOOOOH!

How about a sigh of surprise or delight:
OOOOOOOO!

And to finish up, a deep sigh of satisfaction:
AAAAAAAH!

Note that sighing is a quick and easy antidote to tension.

Sighing is the body's natural way to release tension and get more oxygen.

Sighing exercises the diaphragm, deepens breathing and relaxes tight jaw and throat muscles.

Try a deep sigh whenever you notice tension.

Adapted from *Structured Exercises in Stress Management, vol. 4.*

Autogenics for Deep Relaxation

Warm Hands

Use the power of suggestion to reverse the physical effects of stress. This soothing autogenic routine helps muscles to relax, allowing blood to circulate freely to all parts of the body. It's expecially effective for headaches or insomnia.

Time
5–10 minutes

&&&

Lean back and relax as comfortably as possible... You may want to close your eyes to reduce distractions...

Begin by taking a deep breath... Inhale, filling your lungs with air all the way down to the belly...

Now exhale slowly with a soft "whooshing" sound. Take another deep breath... and imagine as you breathe out that all the tension is leaving your body...

Imagine your hands as warm — relaxed and warm... Say to yourself slowly four times...

My hands are warm... relaxed and warm...

Pause 15 seconds

Now visualize your hands in a bucket of warm water . . .
or comfortably near a roaring fire . . .

Stay with that image as you slowly say to yourself . . .
My hands are warm . . . relaxed and warm . . .

Pause

Make your mental image as vivid as possible as you
warm your hands in this comfortable cozy way . . .
reminding yourself again . . .

My hands are warm . . . relaxed and warm . . .

Pause

As you continue to visualize your hands becoming
warmer and more relaxed . . . perhaps you can even begin
to allow the blood to flow down your arms . . . and into
your hands . . . leaving them feeling warmer and
warmer . . . and more and more relaxed . . .

Let that feeling of warmth and relaxation spread down
your arms and into your hands as you say to yourself . . .

My hands are warm . . . relaxed and warm . . .

Pause

Now allow that pleasant feeling of warmth to spread
throughout your body as you tell yourself . . . I am calm
and relaxed . . .

Pause

Continue to enjoy this feeling of warmth and relaxation as you prepare to turn your attention from the inner you to the outer world...

Before you open your eyes... mentally prepare for your return by saying several times to yourself...

When I open my eyes, I will feel relaxed, fresh, and alert...

Pause

When you are ready... please open your eyes...

Adapted from *Structured Exercises in Stress Management, vol. 3,* available on the CD and audiotape *Warm and Heavy.*

Guided Imagery
for
Relaxation
and
Well-Being

Countdown to Relaxation

Through breathing and visual imagery, learn to relax more deeply. This whole person approach is particularly involving since it combines physical relaxation with visual and auditory stimuli. With regular practice, you will soon be able to condense this process from a 100-countdown to a 10-countdown, eliciting the relaxation response quickly in most situations.

This technique works especially well for falling asleep. Most people will enter sleep or very deep relaxation by the time the countdown is in the 50s.

Time
5–10 minutes

&-&-&

Lean back and relax as comfortably as possible...
You may want to close your eyes as you take a deep breath and focus your attention inward...

Take another deep breath and quickly scan your body for tension. Whenever you notice any tightness, breathe into that area...

And then release the tension as you exhale...

You may even want to sigh as you let go of the tension that has stored up...

Take another deep breath and feel the tension drain away as you exhale...

Continue to breathe deeply as you become more and more relaxed.

Pause 10 seconds.

Now I'd like you to imagine that you are in front of a large movie screen...somewhat like a drive-in theater...

Let the screen fill your entire visual field...As far as you look...up and down...left and right...the empty screen is all you can see.

Notice the color of the screen...Notice its texture...

Now allow the number "100" to appear on the screen...

Notice the shape...color...texture...Perhaps the sound of saying the number...Just notice and appreciate the presence of the number...

Let the number change from "100" to "99"...
Notice how it changes...Does it fall like a card?...
disperse like a mist?...blink out?...melt or dissolve?...
crumble into bits?...just change its form?...

Notice how the numbers are formed...rounded?...
angular?...three dimensional?...Does the color change in some subtle way?...

At your own pace let the numbers continue to change...

Every few relaxing breaths the number can change...
Each time it changes you can relax even more deeply...

*Give people about 3 minutes to count down on their own
before ending the exercise.*

Now it's time to stop counting... Just allow whatever
number is on your screen to disappear and then return
your attention to this room and this group... Take
whatever time you need, knowing that when you open
your eyes you will remain just as comfortable and deeply
relaxed as you now feel.

Adapted from *Structured Exercises in Wellness Promotion, vol. 1,*
available on the CD and audiotape *Countdown.*

Anchoring

The stress response is elicited by whatever cues we perceive as threatening even if they lie only in the past or in fantasy.

The relaxation response is also stimulated by certain cues, such as music, a soothing touch, etc. It too can be stimulated by recollection or by fantasy. We can purposefully train ourselves to relax in response to a specific cue.

To experience the power of learned cues, participants guide one another through a soothing relaxation fantasy and "anchor" the comfortable feelings they experience for later recall and stimulation of the relaxation response.

Time
30 minutes

Materials
Photocopies of the Anchoring Instructions for Guides and Followers.

Introduce participants to the activity, using information from the script description along with the following information:

The purpose of this activity is to connect a series of relaxing experiences and images to a spot on your body. This process is called anchoring. Subsequently touching this spot acts as a cue for eliciting the relaxation response.

Ask participants to form pairs and move to comfortable places in the room. Distribute the Instructions for Guides and Instructions for Followers and ask pairs to determine who will be the guide first and who the follower. Briefly describe the process, and then ask participants to read the instructions thoroughly and proceed at their own pace.

After ten minutes, signal the Guides that time is up. Partners debrief and check the anchoring response as indicated in their instructions. They then change roles and repeat the process.

Submitted by David X Swenson.

Adapted from *Structured Exercises in Stress Management, vol. 2,* available on the CD and audiotape *Stress Escapes.*

INSTRUCTIONS FOR FOLLOWERS

1. Your guide is going to help you visualize a series of especially relaxing scenes from your personal experience or fantasy.

2. During this experience you will need a silent signal to communicate with your partner. Just nod your head to let him know when you have an image clearly in mind and are experiencing peak relaxation.

3. You also need to choose a spot on your body for your partner to use as an "anchor" point for these relaxation visualizations. Most people choose a spot near the knuckle of the index finger. Your guide will touch this spot for you when you indicate peak relaxation. Later you can touch this same spot to elicit feelings of relaxation for yourself.

4. You will be visualizing two or three scenes. Each time you feel yourself relaxing totally into the mood of the scene you will nod to your guide and he will touch you on the anchor spot. This will add each subsequent relaxation experience to those already "anchored" to that spot.

5. When your time is up, describe your experience as completely as you can, paying special attention to the signs of relaxation you notice.

6. Before you switch roles and become the guide, touch your anchor spot yourself and notice the response.

7. Remember, you can add more of your own calming experiences to this special spot by touching your anchor point whenever you're feeling particularly relaxed. Then, when you're under stress, just take a deep breath, touch the anchor point and the relaxing images will again flood into your being.

INSTRUCTIONS FOR GUIDES

1. Begin by asking your partner to show you the exact spot she wants you to use as an "anchor" for her relaxed feelings.

2. Ask your partner to find a comfortable, balanced posture (seated, lying, leaning against the wall).

   Once she is settled ask her to take a deep breath, close her eyes and relax. Tell her to focus on breathing and let go of any tension she feels. Instruct her to continue breathing deeply and to nod her head when she feels quite relaxed.

3. As soon as she nods her head, you are going to help her recall an especially relaxing experience. Your job is to help her make it vivid in her imagination. Your instructions need to guide her in the process, yet be general enough so that she can create the scene for herself.

   You will need to go slowly, allowing time for the images to form in her mind. A nod is always a signal that she is ready to move on.

4. Start by saying: I'd like you to recall a deeply relaxing situation from your personal experience, a time when you felt extremely calm and at peace. Remember everything you can about that time of peaceful relaxation. Bring it alive in your mind.

   While your partner is imaging, you can heighten the sensory visualization by suggesting she notice the colors, hues, shapes and contrasts in her image.

   After a pause you might suggest that she pay attention to the sounds and smells, the temperature, the feeling of the scene around her.

All these suggestions should be made in very general terms so your partner can create the specifics of her scenario without your preferences sneaking in. Try permissive language such as you might notice. Use words suggesting relaxation such as restful, comfortable, easy, calm, peaceful.

5. When the experience is quite realistic and eliciting peak relaxation, your partner should nod. At this point, you should touch her "anchor spot."

6. Ask your partner to recall another relaxing experience or ask her to create in fantasy the most relaxing scene she could possibly imagine. Repeat Steps 4 and 5, helping her enrich the scene with sensory images and anchoring the response to her "spot" when the experience is most intense.

7. Repeat Step 4 and Step 5 with a third relaxation fantasy.

8. Ask your partner to return her awareness outside herself again, back to your interaction. Give her a minute or two to get reoriented and then ask her to describe her experience to you.

9. Sometime during her description reach over and touch the "anchor spot" to test if it really elicits relaxation.

Hot Tub

In this unusual relaxation experience, participants relax in the soothing warmth of an imaginary hot springs as they learn the power of visualization as a tension-reduction strategy.

Time
8–10 minutes

To keep distractions to a minimum, you may want to dim the lights and play soothing music softly in the background.

Invite participants to indulge in a soothing relaxation break.

&&&

Take a minute to get prepared for relaxation.

Take a deep breath and let your body find a comfortable, supported position.

Balance your upper body over your pelvis, put your feet flat on the floor.

Let your hands fall naturally in your lap with your arms supported by your thighs.

Close your eyes and get ready for an imaginery trip to a
relaxing environment.

As you begin to relax...
focus for a moment on your breathing...

Take a deep breath...and as you exhale...
let go of any worries or concerns that you've been
carrying...

Breathe in again...
letting your chest and belly expand as you inhale . . .
And then exhale...with a sigh...as you breathe out...
letting go of any tension you may be feeling...

As you continue to breathe...deeply...and
rhythmically...
feel the air filling every cell in your body...
making you feel lighter and lighter...

Imagine that you are relaxing comfortably...
in a bubbling hot springs...
or in a hot tub or whirlpool...

The steaming water enfolds and surrounds you...
all the way up to your chin...
gently massaging your skin...
with millions of tiny bubbles...
that caress you, and cleanse you...
draining away your tension...and troubles...

Enjoy the warmth...and comfort...
and support...of the water...

Pause.

Notice how your skin tingles...how your face feels
full...

how the pores all over your body...
open up to the healing warmth of the bubbling water...

Pause.

Listen to the sound of the bubbles...
as they percolate through the water...
and gurgle to the surface...

Every part of your body is totally relaxed...
supported by the warm water and the tiny bubbles...

Your arms and legs...feel heavy...and warm...
and relaxed...yet buoyant...

The warmth of the water...
penetrates every part of your body...
allowing you to unwind...and let go...

Allow the cleansing warmth of the water...
to drain away any tension or discomfort that you are
feeling...

Watch that tension evaporate...
as the bubbles rise to the surface...
leaving you totally at peace...

Stay and enjoy the warmth and relaxation of the
water...
enjoy the feelings of comfort...and calm...
for as long as you wish...

When you are ready...
return to the routine of your day...

refreshed...
revitalized...
unworried...
taking the peace of this place...with you...

Adapted from *Structured Exercises in Stress Management, vol. 4,* available on the CD and audiotape *Daydreams 1: Getaways.*

*T*rouble Bubbles

This brief visualization encourages participants to get rid of negative feelings by imagining them as bubbles that rise and blow away.

Time
5 minutes

&&&

Find a place where your body feels comfortable and supported...
Close your eyes...
and allow your whole body to relax...
Breathe in and out slowly...
deeply... evenly...

Become aware of any bad feelings you have...
as you review what has happened to you today...
They may be feelings of sadness...
loneliness... anxiety... anger... or guilt...
Tune in to whatever undesirable feelings you recall...

Pause 5 seconds

Now let these bad feelings...

and the thoughts that go with them...
become bubbles in your mind...

Pause 15 seconds

Imagine as you exhale...
that you blow these bubbles of bad feelings away...
Try exhaling with your mouth open...
so you hear the sound of the air rushing out...
as you blow away the bubbles...

Pause 15 seconds

Continue to breathe and blow...
until you can no longer see the bubbles or feel the
feelings...
Some have broken...
others have drifted out of sight...
You feel free and light...
very much alive . . .

Pause 15 seconds

Now, when you are ready, slowly return to your
surroundings...
carrying this feeling of lightness and energy back with
you...

Pause 5 seconds

When you open your eyes you will feel refreshed and free.

Adapted from *Structured Exercises in Stress Management, vol. 5,*
available on the CD and audiotape *Worry Stoppers.*

$\mathcal{S}$ anctuary

An imaginary sanctuary can offer a brief retreat from daily stresses. This technique is also useful for people who have trouble sleeping.

Time
15–20 minutes

Make a few introductory comments about guided imagery and relaxation, then lead the group through a 3–5 minute warm-up relaxation routine focused on breathing or progressive muscle relaxation.

When participants have settled down and are breathing deeply, guide the group through the sanctuary experience.

&&&

Begin to shift your focus of awareness inside...

Visualize in your mind's eye a large movie screen, noting the top, bottom, sides and texture of the screen...

Visualize your own personal sanctuary—a special place to which you can travel for a brief respite; a place where you can relax, enjoy your leisure and learn in your own way how to take time out from the stimulation that crowds your life...

Focus on your movie screen and wait for such a personal sanctuary to appear...

The place that begins to take shape on the screen in your mind may be a real or mythical setting. It may be out in nature or inside a healing temple from ages ago...

Just allow the image to form and try not to force it in any way...

As the picture becomes clearer, step into the scene. Once inside the scene, attend with great curiosity and detail to the sensory qualities of the place:

gentle sounds...peaceful silence...fragrances... breezes...textures...colors...shapes...

Explore your sanctuary space with all of your senses until it becomes vivid and complete, enjoying the calm and quiet.

Pause 3 minutes.

Since you now know the way to this special place, you may return at any time you wish...

Temporarily say good-bye to your sanctuary and return to the room...

Submitted by David X Swenson.

Adapted from *Structured Exercises in Wellness Promotion, vol. 1,* available on the CD and audiotape *Daydreams 3: Relaxing Retreats.*

$\mathcal{B}$reathing Elements

While focusing their attention on conscious breathing, participants draw strength from visualizing images of nature and imagining a connection with the four basic elements: earth, air, fire, and water.

Time
5–10 minutes

Instruct participants to relax comfortably in a chair with eyes closed, spine straight, feet flat on the floor, and palms face up in their laps.

After they are quiet and settled, read the script slowly in a relaxed voice, allowing ample transition time between each separate image.

&&&

Earth
Inhale through your nose...exhale through your nose...
Focus on physical energy...

Visualize a tree . . . with strong roots and full branches . . .

As you inhale, draw in strength . . . health . . .
security . . . power . . .

As you exhale affirm to yourself:
I draw strength from the earth . . .
I am grounded like a tree.

Water
Inhale through your nose . . . exhale through your
mouth . . .
Focus on mental energy . . .
Visualize a flowing stream . . . with clear, cool water . . .

As you inhale, draw in freedom . . . clarity . . .
spontaneity . . .

As you exhale affirm:
I draw freedom from the water . . .
I am flowing like a stream.

Fire
Inhale through your mouth . . . exhale through your nose . . .
Focus on emotional energy . . .
Visualize the radiant sunshine . . . with its brightness and
heat . . .

As you inhale, draw in warmth . . . light . . . love . . . joy . . .
laughter . . .

As you exhale affirm:
I draw warmth from the sun . . .
I am radiant like the sun.

Air
Inhale through your mouth...exhale through your
mouth...
Focus on spiritual energy...
Visualize the open air...the wind...the clouds...

As you inhale, draw in awareness . . . expansion . . .

As you exhale affirm:
I draw openness from the wind...
I am expanding like the air.

Allow your breathing to return to normal...

Begin to stretch very slowly...
Open your eyes when you are ready...
Bring your attention back into the room.

Adapted from *Structured Exercises in Wellness Promotion, vol. 3.*

$\mathcal{S}$ensory Relaxation Suggestions

By focusing on sensory awareness, participants discover that they can reduce tension through the use of imagination and attention to sensation.

Time
5–10 minutes

Invite participants to prepare for an unusual relaxation experience, with these introductory comments:

Find a comfortable position.

I will be reading a number of suggestions that will require that you use your imagination to tune in to your sensations

There is no right or wrong way to respond. Listen to each statement and allow yourself to respond naturally. Don't try to make anything happen. Simply notice your sensations.

Read some or all of the suggestions, pausing 15 seconds between each statement so participants can attend to the suggested sensation. Be sure to include the first two and the last four suggestions.

Pause 15 seconds after each statement

&&&

Gently let your eyes close. (pause)

Allow yourself to sit heavily in your chair. (pause)

Imagine the space between your ears.

Become aware of the distance between your ears.

Become aware of how close your breath comes to the back of your eyes every time you inhale.

Become aware of the space within your mouth.

Notice the position of your tongue within your mouth.

Feel your lips becoming soft.

Imagine a warm spring breeze against your cheek.

Imagine the sun radiating on the back of your neck.

Expand that warmth down your entire back.

Feel the weight of your arms pulling down your shoulders.

Become aware of one of your arms being more relaxed than the other.

Feel the space between your fingers.

Feel a warm breeze brush against your fingers.

Make your legs feel as limp as a rag doll.

Feel the floor beneath your feet.

Try to feel like you are becoming a few inches taller by allowing yourself to stretch out through the bottom of your feet.

Imagine that your arms are growing.

As you inhale, pretend that the air is puffing you up like a balloon.
As you exhale, feel like a balloon that is slowly losing its air.

Now picture your lungs as birds' wings.
As you slowly inhale, picture the wings rising gracefully.
As you slowly exhale, imagine the wings lowering smoothly.

Feel yourself floating as if on a cloud.

Imagine that you are looking at something very far away.

See in your mind's eye a beautiful object suspended a few feet in front of you.

Imagine that you can hear a seashell at your ear.

Imagine your head sinking into a soft, fluffy pillow.

Check to see if your feel tension anywhere in your body. Send mental messages to those areas to eliminate the tension.

As you inhale, imagine your breath is sending energy to all areas of your body.

As you exhale, imagine any tension is leaving your body through your fingertips and toes.

Allow yourself to sit where you are and enjoy your state of relaxation. (longer pause)

Allow your eyes to open. Open them now, and be wide awake and very comfortable.

Submitted by Janet A. Simons and Donald B Irwin.

Adapted from *Structured Exercises in Wellness Promotion, vol. 4;* available on the CD and audiotape *Stress Escapes.*

*N*ight Sky

In this awe-inspiring guided image, participants search the heavens for a sense of cosmic meaning and connectedness. In doing so, they tap into their creative energies and explore inner truths.

Time
8–10 minutes

Invite participants to indulge in an inspirational awareness-expanding exploration of a starry night.

Settle back into your seat and gently close your eyes.

Imagine that you are seated in a darkened Omnimax theater with a giant screen above and all around you.

Relax comfortably into the support of your plush reclining seat.

Take a few deep breaths to launch yourself on a cosmic adventure.

As you read the script, don't hurry. Visualize the images yourself and enjoy the process as you soar through the script.

&&&

As you relax yourself and prepare to enjoy the wide
expanse of the night sky...

Begin to close your eyes...and let go...

Notice any part of your body...that feels constricted
and small...

As you breathe...imagine filling that tight area with
air...letting it expand as you breathe in...
and as you breathe out . . . let this area relax . . .

Feel yourself open . . . and expand . . .
as you let go of the tension . . .

Once again...
allow yourself to expand as you breathe in...
and to relax as you breathe out...

Imagine that you are looking up...at the night sky...
You are outside...away from the lights...
The night is clear...and calm...
The stars are shining...the evening holds a quiet magic.

You notice where you are...
You notice the season of the year...

You are alone...but safe and calm...in the quiet of the
night...
You are quiet...filled with a sense of awe...
As you gaze on the expanse of the night...
you notice the brilliant diamond lights...that blanket
the heavens.

You notice a layering of the expanse...
stars that puncture the darkness with clarity...
others that dim...
still others only subliminal suggestions...
mere hints of the thousands and millions of stars not
seen...
that extend into the infinite expanse...which your eyes
cannot reach.

You look over the whole sky...
and you notice what you see...
as you look...from horizon...to horizon.

You focus on a cluster of stars...
Stars appear...at the edge of your vision...
You focus on them...but they disappear as you do...

Your eyes wander...
a falling star streaks across the darkness...
and before you get focused...
it disappears and vaporizes into a memory...
a memory that touched you...
a memory that you never got hold of...

Your eyes focus on stars that sparkle...
on stars that remain constant...
on stars that come in and out of focus...
seeming to disappear, then reappear at will...

Your eyes come to rest...

You focus on nothing...
But you take in the sense of the whole...
and you feel the expanse...
You sense the unlimited infinite...

without known boundaries...that goes on forever...

And you breathe...deeply...
Taking this expanse into yourself...fully...

You let go of your own boundaries...
you expand into the night sky...
you live for the moment in the wonder of the sky...

And you let go of your boundaries...
connected with awe...to the expanse...
that always holds more than you can see...
that seems to be bigger than your imagination...

And you gaze in awe...at the sky...
which goes on without ending...of which you
are a part...

And allow yourself...to fill...
to expand...with the wonder of the moment.

When you are ready...
allow yourself to return...from this vision.

Still open...unconstrained...relaxed...
having been expanded...
having been touched...
by the infinite expanse of the clear night sky...
that extends out forever.

Adapted from *Structured Exercises in Wellness Promotion, vol. 5,*
available on the CD and audiotape *Daydreams 1: Getaways.*

Guided Imagery
for
Insight
and
Change

Channel Surfing

Participants use imaginary powers to tune into a chosen year of their life and watch themselves on TV, practicing creative visualization as a tool for insight and a catalyst for personal growth. They also enhance their self-esteem through the awareness of personal perception and the power of choice.

Time
10–15 minutes

This process assumes that participants have had some experience with or preparation for guided imagery.

Introduce the visualization by announcing that participants will have the opportunity to visit any year of their life— past, present or future — and focus on real or imagined events occurring during that time of their life.

Review basic principles of guided imagery.

Close your eyes, take a few deep breaths, and allow your body to relax and your mind to clear.

Be open to your inner vision. Allow images to unfold without trying to direct or control them.

Remember, you are in charge. You can stop the process at any time, simply by opening your eyes.

&·&·&

Take a deep breath and slowly blow the air out in a big sigh, letting yourself relax as much as possible

Gently close your eyes and allow your mind to empty, letting any thoughts or distractions float easily away as you allow your inner vision to waken.

Imagine in your mind's eye that you are sitting in front of a television set with a rather large screen.

Feel the remote control in your hand and be aware that anytime you wish you may turn the set on or off or turn the volume up or down. So you are in charge of how intensely you become involved in whatever you choose to watch.

Also notice the channel indicator with its large display numbers. This special indicator includes numbers to represent every year of your life from the time of your birth at 0 to your present age and on into the future.

Now notice the fine tuning knob. This little dial allows you to tune in to actual months, weeks, or days during any given year of your life.

Take another deep breath. And as you breathe out, press the button on the remote control and turn on the television. The channel indicator is automatically set at 30.

Begin counting up or down as you slowly switch channels until you find a year you would like to watch.

Pause 15 seconds.

When you have found a year that appeals to you, settle back and watch the show. Observe whatever images and sounds come to you from that year of your life. Continue to watch and observe as long as you want.

Pause 1 minute or more.

At a moment of your choosing, switch to the channel for your present age and then turn off the television.

As the screen darkens in your mind, slowly open your eyes and return your attention to the present.

Submitted by Richard Boyum

Adapted from *Instant Icebreakers.*

*G*etting Out of My Box

In this reflective exercise, participants examine the chronically stressful situations in their lives, the painful life circumstances that may limit them.

Time
20 minutes

Distribute blank paper and pencils, and then introduce the goal of this exercise.

Make yourself as comfortable as possible, close your eyes, and prepare to explore the boxes that constrain you.

Some of those boxes may be:
    Expectations and beliefs
    Habits
    People
    Employment
    Personal failures and limitations
    Others

Read the script slowly, taking at least 10 minutes, with ample pauses that allow participants time to imagine what you have suggested.

&·&·&

Begin to become quiet within yourself...
listen to your insides...
relax...and concentrate on the steady...
deep...rhythm of your breathing...

When you breathe in...fill yourself with air...
fill you belly with air...expand...

When you breathe out...let yourself collapse...
from the inside...like a balloon...
with the air...going out...

Imagine you are taking a walk...
on a beautiful path...on a green hillside...
a setting like the Sound of Music...
beautiful green hills...

As you walk...along the path...
you notice some flowers...by the wayside...

You feel...the breeze on your face...
you are at peace...and free...
and enjoying yourself...

As you walk...you come to a fork in the path...
one path goes right...one goes left...
one is stony...and edged with grass...
the other is wide...with a smooth surface...

You take one of those paths...and continue your
walk...

As your walk continues...
you notice you are approaching...a woods...

You come closer...and notice the trees...
you keep walking...and enter the forest...

As you walk...the forest grows thicker...
the light becomes dimmer...
the greens rich and dark...the air cool...

As you continue...to walk in the forest...
you notice a large box...on the side of the path...

You stop...and you look...
noticing the details of this box...

You look carefully at the box...
noticing its size...and its shape...and its color...
and you walk around it...slowly...
noticing how it is made...

Then...just for fun...
you decide...to try crawling...into the box...

You crawl in...and look at the inside...of the box...
and notice the colors...the shapes...
the smells...inside of the box...

You experiment by shutting the door to the box...
shutting it slowly...so the light slowly fades...

You close it slowly...you close it completely...
and see the crack of light...slowly fade and disappear...
as the door shuts completely...

Now you are inside the box...
and it is dark...and you are still...
and you notice how you feel...

You notice the size of the box inside...
you notice whether you want to sit quietly...
or move...exploring the corners of the box...

You notice the quiet in the box...
and you notice how you feel...

Soon...you realize that you are ready...
to leave the box...

It is now time to escape...
imagine how you escape...what do you try first?...
where do you push?...how hard?...how long?...

Now you are out...you have escaped from the box . . .
you notice your feelings...
and you think back over the effort...
of leaving...the box...
and how you escaped...

Now you are outside the box...
once again in the light of the forest...
and you notice the sounds...and the feelings...

And you walk around the box once again...
checking it out...carefully...
so you can remember...all the details

How is it sitting...
is it still the way it was when you found it?...
or has it moved?...

Is it still intact?...
or have the sides been broken out?...

You notice...and remember...

then you prepare yourself...to say good-bye...
to the box...

Because it is now time to move on...
but you keep the clear memory...of your experience...
with you...as you walk away...from the box...

And you walk...down the path...
only a short distance...
before you come out of the woods...
back into the bright sunlight...of the day...

And you come out of your journey...
back into the bright sunlight...of this room...

And you slowly...come out of your journey...back
into this room...

Carrying with you...back into this room...
the clear memory...of your box...
and your experience...with it...

As you come back into this room...
come back just far enough...
to take your worksheet and begin drawing a picture...
of your box...

Come back to this room...
pick up your worksheet...and start drawing your box...

Recall and draw all the details you can...
pay attention to the size...and color...
the construction...the shape...

Note how the box was when you saw it first...
and how it was when you left it...

Recall how it felt for you...
on the outside...and on the inside...

Embellish your drawing with all the details you can...

Allow 2–4 minutes for participants to draw their boxes and another 5–10 minutes for them to share what they learned in a large or small group discussion.

Adapted from *Structured Exercises in Stress Management, vol. 1.*

Magic Door

In this guided fantasy, participants use the "magic" of visualization to prepare themselves for a new learning experience as they explore the power of visualization as a creative model for approaching problems.

Time
10–15 minutes

Invite participants to join in an unusual warm-up that will help them remove themselves from the hectic here-and-now and prepare for an adventure.

Instruct them to find a comfortable position with feet on the floor and eyes closed. Then read the script slowly, allowing plenty of time to visualize each image and movement.

&&&

As we begin, take a deep breath...
and slowly bring your awareness into your feet...
Now let your awareness rise up your lower legs...
into your knees... up into your thighs... your pelvis...
stomach... chest... shoulders...
down into your arms... hands... fingers...
up into your neck... and head...

Allow your face to relax and concentrate on your breathing...

Breathe slowly and softly...like a child sleeping...
As you breathe...take yourself back to your childhood...
to a time when you were going to sleep and everything felt good...
It is a very peaceful evening...
the stars are shining and you are cozily tucked into bed...

Although you are almost asleep, your curiosity is awake and you begin to wonder about the closet in your room...
Somehow you know there is a magical door hidden in the back of the closet...
You get out of bed to investigate...and there it is...
hidden behind a curtain at the back...

You pull back the curtain...open the hidden door...
and with a great sense of adventure,
enter the semi-darkness on the other side...
There is a dim light to guide you as you begin to walk down a long spiral staircase...
winding down, down, down...
As you descend, your curiosity grows and grows.
You continue going down...slowly...
taking your time...and being careful to keep your balance...

Finally you come to the bottom...
which opens into a large cavern filled with water...
At the edge of the water is a boat...

tied to the base of the steps you have just climbed
down...
You enter the boat, untying it and releasing it from its
dock...

You lie down in the bottom of the boat
and wrap yourself in a comfortable blanket...
The boat begins drifting with a natural current
that carries it across the waters of the cavern...
Its natural rocking movement is very relaxing...
The water laps gently against your boat with a soothing
rhythm...

At the other side of the cavern
your boat enters a large and long tunnel...
The current moves more quickly now,
taking you far into the depths of the tunnel . . .
until off in the distance you see a light...
The light grows as you move more quickly toward the
end of the tunnel...
and at last you emerge into full daylight...

You find yourself in a beautiful sunlit world...
with lovely rolling hills...
bright green and full of flowers, birds and flourishing
nature...
You can smell the fragrances of the different flowers
and hear the birds singing and the bees buzzing
as on a warm summer day...

Your boat is now drifting toward the shore...
and gently lands so that you can easily get up
and explore the new world before you...
You walk slowly up a hill to a large tree at the top...

You sit down under the tree...
and looking around at this wonderful new land...
you prepare yourself for great adventure ...

When you are ready to begin...gently open your
eyes...

Submitted by Neil Young.

Adapted from *Structured Exercises in Wellness Promotion, vol. 4.*

Treasure Chest

In this colorful guided fantasy, participants discover a treasure chest containing a gift they need. In doing so, they synthesize and begin to own new ideas they have learned. The fantasy offers a relaxing wrap-up to any session.

Time
15–20 minutes

Before beginning the fantasy, decide what gift you want participants to discover in the treasure chest. Depending on your goals, you might choose a gift such as relaxation or a positive outlook.

&&&

Place your feet flat on the floor...scoot your seat against the back of the chair...place your hands comfortably in your lap.

Take a deep breath...let it go...take another deep breath...let it go...take another deep breath...

Close your eyes...Let your body relax...allow yourself to breathe deeply and heavily...as you inhale, inhale relaxation . . . as you exhale, exhale tension . . . Allow yourself to be calm and relaxed.

Now imagine yourself in a field of red . . . run through the field of red . . . see the poppies . . . see the cardinals . . . Allow yourself to experience red.

Let people experience red for about 45 seconds.

Then go into a field of orange . . . allow yourself to experience orange . . . see the oranges . . . see the orange flowers . . .

Allow yourself the experience of the field of orange . . . allow yourself to smell it . . . What does it taste like?

Again wait for approximately 45 seconds.

Now imagine yourself in a field of yellow. See the yellow flowers . . . see the daisies and daffodils . . . see the canaries . . . and anything else yellow . . .

Totally experience yellow . . . What does it sound like? . . . What does it feel like? . . . Immerse yourself in yellow.

Wait 45 seconds.

Then go into a field of green . . . experience the incredible number of shades of green . . . Let the green surround you . . . experience the field of green.

Wait 45 seconds.

Imagine yourself in a field of blue, sky blue . . . allow yourself to relax in blue . . . see the blue flowers . . . breathe in the blueness . . .

Experience what blue feels like.

Wait 45 seconds.

Now imagine a field of dark blue, indigo...see the bluebirds...see the blueberries...surround yourself with that dark blue...Allow that dark blue to surround you...What does it taste like?...What does it smell like?

Wait 45 seconds.

Then imagine yourself in a field of purple, deep royal purple...see the violets...see the other purple flowers...

Let yourself experience the purple...what it feels like... what it sounds like...what it tastes like.

Wait 45 seconds.

Now imagine that all the colors become one and turn into a white light surrounding you...let the white light penetrate and envelop you.

Now you notice you're on a path in a forest...allow yourself to walk through the forest...until you become aware that you're coming to a clearing...

In the next sentence, nsert a topic relevant to the course such as stress, relationships, humor, worrying, grief, health, coping.

There's a pond in the clearing...by the pond is your favorite tree...Let yourself sit by the tree...and think about (the topic of the session).

The pond is clear and deep... you can see the bottom ... and you notice a chest at the bottom of the pond.

Now imagine yourself—even if you can't swim, it's okay, you're safe ... just imagine yourself diving into the pond and bringing up the treasure chest... bring it back over to where you are by the tree.

In just a minute, I'll ask you to open the treasure chest... Inside there will be a gift regarding (the chosen topic)... The gift will be a word... or a picture... or a thought... or a presence...

Don't try to make anything happen... just let it come to you... if you don't get something during this process... just let that be okay... it will come to you later on today... or in your sleep.

Now, open the box... and see what gift is inside... and let the gift talk to you... telling you what it is for and what it means.

Wait approximately 30 seconds.

If you have any questions, ask the gift now.

Wait approximately 30 seconds.

Now you have a choice... In just a minute, I'll ask you to do one of two things... You can either close the box and put it back in the water ...

Or... you can put your hands out in front of you... and imagine the treasure chest shrinking... shrinking small enough to fit into your hands ... Then imagine opening your heart... and putting the treasure chest inside your heart for safe-keeping...

Do one of those right now.

Wait 30 seconds.

Now, get up and start walking along the path...and count from 1 to 5...when you get to 5, you'll be back in this room.

Adapted from *Structured Exercises in Stress Management, vol. 2.*

R̸est in Peace

In this unusual visualization, participants lay to rest negative attitudes, perceptions, and patterns that cause them stress, identifying adaptive patterns that have outlived their uselessness.

Time
15–20 minutes

Distribute paper and pencils to participants and introduce the basic principles underlying the exercise.

Most of us carry around leftover thoughts, ideas, beliefs, feelings or attitudes that helped us get through a particular difficult situation. In the short run, attitudes such as hostility, despair, denial, perfectionism, cynicism, and insensitivity can be effective stress managers, but in the long run they are stress producers rather than reducers.

Periodically we need to clean house by taking stock of our response repertoire and getting rid of those patterns that may once have been effective but now result in negative consequences.

For example, anger toward your parents may have once

been an essential tool to help you separate from them. However, holding on to this antagonism into adulthood can be stressful — and can interfere with the development of satisfying mutual relationships as adults.

We are going to experiment with a visualization process that can be applied whenever you want to let go of unwanted stress or dysfunctional coping patterns.

&·&·&

Close your eyes, take a deep breath or two, and relax.

Take a moment now to tune in to yourself and tune out whatever may be distracting...
Take a deep breath...and let it out with a soft sigh...

Focus on your easy breathing that quiets and calms you...
Take another deep breath...and as you breathe out...
let go of whatever is cluttering your mind...

As you continue to breathe freely and easily...
allow yourself to become aware of some of the negative attitudes...perceptions...feelings...patterns...
that may be causing you unwanted stress...

Even though these patterns were once essential or effective in managing your life...you need to let go of them now...
lay them to rest...so that you can have peace...

Let this procession of negative thoughts, feelings, attitudes pass before your mind's eye...
Try to give each image a name or symbol so that you can bring it into sharper focus...

*Allow some time here for people to get in touch with these
negative stressors and visualize them.*

Now imagine yourself in a funeral parlor...
In a room with a special container...
that can be closed and sealed for burial...
Notice that the container is open now...
ready to receive any negative thoughts...
any attitudes or feelings that are distressing to you...
All those unhealthy patterns you would like to give up...

Now imagine holding all these unwanted thoughts and
beliefs in your hands...
Then one-by-one place them in the container
so you never have to see them again...

As you are putting your unwanted relics in the container
and preparing to close the cover...
consider who you would like to join you in this special
place...
to witness this surrender...

Imagine that these friends are now standing with you...
supporting you... remembering with you...
mourning with you the passing of these comfortable old
habits...

*Pause here long enough for participants
to imagine the arrival of their supporting cast.*

Now it's time to close the cover of the container...
and journey to the cemetery where a special place
has been prepared to accept your container...
This could be a crypt, or a grave, or a monument...

whatever seems right to hold your burdens...
Invite the others to join you as you take your container
to its final resting place...

Once you and the others reach the cemetery...
place your container into the grave and cover it...
or close the door of the crypt...

Allow yourself to experience all of your feelings...
as you say "goodbye" to these parts of you...
as you feel the support of those around you...

Imagine now a marker being placed on the grave...
A marker that commemorates each of the things
that you are putting to rest...

Pause here for this image to form.

Now imagine yourself and your companions
slowly withdrawing from the grave site...

Know that at any time you choose...
you can return to this site in your imagination...
and ponder what is buried here that you no longer need...

Take a moment to complete your journey back to this
place...
no longer bearing the burdens you have put to rest...

Enjoy the peace and calm and freedom
as you return your awareness to this place and the people
around you...

Stretch a little...take a few deep breaths...
and prepare to capture some of your images on paper...

*Instruct participants to use their peace of paper like a
headstone or grave marker and to write on it the stressful
attitudes, feelings, and patterns that they decided to bury.*

Submitted by Richard Boyum.

Adapted from *Structured Exercises in Stress Management, vol. 4,*
available on the CD and audiotape *Worry Stoppers.*

Meditation for Calming and Centering

*C*lear the Deck

In this guided fantasy, participants mentally identify
worries and concerns that are occupying their minds and
set them aside so they can be fully present. This tension
reducing technique can be used in anxiety-provoking
situations.

Time
5–10 minutes

*Introduce the script by commenting on how incredibly
active our minds are and the difficulty many people have in
shifting gears. We hold on to the concerns, worries, and
feelings of one situation even while we're already launched
into the next.*

&&&

Shift into a comfortable position... Close your eyes and
take several deep breaths...

Now begin to turn your attention inward...

I'd like you to take a few minutes to focus on the various
concerns, preoccupations, worries that you have brought
with you today (to this class, workshop, etc...).

There may be any number of things that are on your mind—whether you remembered to unplug the coffee pot before you left the house this morning...the unfinished conversation that you had with someone... errands you need to run when you leave here...the project at work or school that's due tomorrow...plans you're making for the weekend...

So take a moment to really focus on what these concerns are for you—develop a mental list...

To the extent that these concerns are occupying your thoughts — making claims on your energy — you are not able to be fully present, here and now for this experience...

Probably, there is nothing that you can do during the next (___ minutes/hours) about these concerns, except to worry...and that will distract you from all you can be learning here...So let's put those worries away for awhile...

I'd like you to create in your mind a box...with a lid on it...and a lock and a key...The box can be any size and shape...but it needs to be large enough and strong enough to hold all the concerns you've identified...

Take a moment to visualize this box as clearly as you can...The box is before you now, with the lid open...

Now I'd like you to put each of your concerns in the box, one-by-one...don't forget any...

As you are doing this, tell yourself, "There is nothing I can do about this for now...and so I'm going to put

this concern away in a safe and secure box—for now—
while I'm here. I know I can come back later, and
reclaim all of my concerns..."

Pause for 1 minute.

When you've put all your preoccupations and concerns
in the box, I'd like you to close the lid and lock it with
your key...

Now I'd like you to put your key in your pocket or
somewhere else for safekeeping...

At the end of this experience, you can unlock your box
and pick up where you left off...

When you're ready, slowly open your eyes and come
back here...

Adapted from *Structured Exercises in Stress Management, vol. 1.*

Centering Meditation

Participants experience the quieting process of
meditation and the focusing power of visualization in
this guided fantasy. They find calm, peace, and a sense
of inner vision as they learn the principles of meditation
and imagery as skills for relaxation.

Time
20-30 minutes

Materials
Paper and pencils

*Introduce the exercise by describing the importance of
relaxation as an antidote to stress—both as a remedy and as
a preventive measure. Note that this skill-building
experience uses elements of two powerful techniques for
inducing a relaxed state. Then go on to describe the process
and power of meditation and guided imagery.*

Meditation may be the most wholistic of all stress
management skills since it involves sensory awareness,
physical relaxation, surrender of thought processes and
focusing on the life force through breathing and
contemplation.

The key elements needed for effective meditation include:

   &   A quiet environment that's free from distraction;

   &   A comfortable position that can be maintained easily for 20 minutes;

   &   A phrase, sound or object to focus on so that distracting thoughts will pass; and

   &   An open and passive attitude, accepting whatever the experience brings.

Scientists have discovered that the hypothalamus (the area of the brain that gathers information input from the senses) responds to symbolic stimuli almost as well as to the real thing. Just as a terrifying movie can provoke our stress reactions, visualizing a peaceful scene will calm our bodies down!

If we practice, we can learn to trigger the relaxation response almost instantly just by using our imaginations.

Invite participants to join in the centering meditation and describe the activity:

This relaxation routine combines breathing, visual imagery and some aspects of meditation in a process of physical and mental centering.

The first part consists of a quieting process to get our energy centered. We will then take an imaginary walk in the forest.

The last step involves some writing.

Distribute paper and pencils, Instruct participants to relax in their chairs and close their eyes. Turn on soft music and slowly read the Centering Meditation script. To pace yourself, take a deep breath at every " . . . " and pause between sections.

&&&

We are sitting in quiet...and calm...
Letting the core become clear...
Letting the thoughts slow their pace...
Letting the breath become regular and slow...
Letting the self become still...

We are sitting in quiet...and calm...
Letting the breath become steady and deep...
Letting energies that were once chasing madly
focus inward and rest...
within the stillness of our center...
Letting energies come to rest
upon the steady rhythm of our breathing...

Breathing at the center, our breath becomes deeper...
Breathing at the quiet and calm of our core
our breath becomes pure and clear...

Our breathing is free...and regular...
Our breathing finds it easy to come...and go...
on its own...without our effort...

Our thoughts become quiet...
Wandering thoughts come to rest...
Our feelings become one...one flow of experience...
All rests on the regular rhythm of our steady
breathing...

that moves into our soul...
Bringing peace... and quiet...
Bringing healing to our core...

We are centered... we are quiet...
All parts connected...
Connected together... by the rhythm of our steady
breathing...

We are clear... and we know clearly... and deeply...
We know peace...
As breathing moves... in... and out...
at the center of our being...
The core... waits calmly...
for the quiet . . . of the breathing...
to bring it healing life...

I am aware of seeing beyond my eyes...
of hearing with more than my ears...
of knowing outside of my mind...
I see and know truth at the core of my being...
And I wait... and watch... in quiet... and calm...
Aware only of my steady, regular breathing...

As I wait... I find myself in a forest...
A forest of trees spread far apart with large trunks...
The trees are so tall they soar above me...
The huge canopy of branches overlapping as a ceiling to
cover me and block out the bright sunlight...

The sun shining so brightly above...
cannot get through to the forest floor where I stand...
Where I walk it is dark...
Where I walk on the floor of the forest... it is quiet...

The quiet surrounds me...as I listen to the stillness...
The silence follows me...as I move slowly through the
forest...

I listen to the presence around me...
I feel the power of the quiet that surrounds me...
And I know I am no longer alone...

As I watch...I notice a small bush...
It is unlike anything else in the forest...
It is glowing...gently...
Its glowing lights up the darkness of the forest...
As it hovers...barely touching the ground...

It glows before me...
Its flowers twinkle with a special light
and its glowing is strong...and even...
Showing no signs of diminishing...
Showing no source of power...
The bush glows...
with a soft brightness...that comes from within...

I am standing deep in the forest...
It is dark at the floor of the forest...
But I am touched...and surrounded by a soft light
that comes from the bush...
It reaches me...touches me...gently...

I feel the soft quality of being that comes from its
light...
I am touched by a gentle power that does not
diminish...
The glowing bush is part of me...
It glows within me...
It enters my heart...and burns steadily...

The glowing bush in the woods bathes me with its soft
light...
The bush will stay with me...

The glowing bush enlightens my core
at the very center of my being...
where my breathing maintains its regular steady
rhythm . . .
At this center of my being the bush lights my heart ...
and shows me truth...

As I stand before the bush my center is quiet...
and calm...My center is light...

As I stand before it...
I become aware I am no longer alone...
A wise, kind person is with me...one whom I trust...
A wise person...very gentle and caring...
In the quiet...the wise one speaks to me...
Speaks about the bush...about life...about me...
And I listen...And I respond...

And the wise one speaks...
And I listen...and respond...
Speaking...and listening...
Listening...and speaking...

As our dialogue continues . . .
I experience the growing of wisdom in me...
Wisdom...from my friend...from the bush...
from within me...
A clarity and knowledge of truth grows in me...

Listening...and speaking...speaking and listening...
I am being touched...

Pause

As you are ready...
slowly come back into the room,
just enough to make some notes of the dialogue...
between you and your wise friend...

Write it like a play with your friend speaking first...
and then write your response...

Pause 3-10 minutes while people write

Take just a minute now
to finish up whatever you're working on...
Then return your attention to this room...

*Allow 3–5 minutes for people to write their dialogues.
Leave the music playing softly in the background, while
participants write down their conversations. Then ask
participants to complete the portion they are working on
and return their attention to the group.*

*Finally, invite any who are willing to read their dialogues
aloud to the entire group.*

*Reading these dialogues aloud can be an extremely powerful
process. Be patient and wait for volunteers. Do not let people
talk about or explain their dialogues. Ask them to read what
they have written without additional comment. Do not
comment or permit discussion. Simply listen to the dialogue,
thank the sharer, and move to the next. When all who wish to
read their dialogues have done so, this exercise is concluded.*

Adapted from *Structured Exercises in Stress Management, vol. 3,*
available on the CD and audiotape *Spiritual Centering.*

$\mathcal{B}$reathing Meditation

In this centering activity, which combines regular breathing with mental affirmations, participants learn to center their attention and quiet their thoughts as they focus on positive health images.

Time
1–2 minutes

Begin by giving instructions for the Breathing Meditation.

This is an exercise in personal centering affirmation. You will be mentally repeating an affirming phrase when you inhale, and a companion phrase as you exhale.

&&&

Close your eyes and take a deep breath. As you inhale, say silently to yourself, "I close my eyes..."

Pause for people to repeat the words internally.

As you exhale, say to yourself, "...and bring my awareness inside."

From the list of Centering Phrases, choose several that are appropriate to the group and context, and guide participants through the mental affirmation process. Don't rush. Lead the group through 3 or 4 slow repetitions before moving on to the next pair of phrases.

Centering Phrases

On the inhaling breath:	On the exhaling breath:
I deepen my breathing	and quiet my thoughts.
I allow my body to be still	and relax my muscles.
I focus into my center	and release my tensions. (or frustration, anxiety, fear, expectations)
I allow health to flow	and let go of disease. (or pain, infection, fatigue, discomfort, toxins)
I open my heart	and free my spirit.
I flow with life	I am one with all.

Submitted by Martha Belknap.

Adapted from *Structured Exercises in Wellness Promotion, vol. 1.*

$\mathcal{W}$ellness Meditation

The cleansing breaths of this affirming visualization reinforce the mind/body/spirit connection in well-being and allow participants to find inner harmony and peace.

This visualization is especially effective just before a break or at the close of a meeting. Leave the music playing for several minutes after the end of the meditation, allowing people to luxuriate in their peaceful feelings.

Time
15 minutes

Introduce the exercise with a few comments on health and wholeness.

The goal of wellness is to experience your body, mind, and spirit interacting in a harmony that promotes wholeness and well-being.

A balanced diet, regular exercise, effective stress management, and other healthy lifestyle decisions contribute to this whole person well-being.

We can heighten our experience of the synergy of the whole by engaging in regular centering meditation that draws the body/mind/spirit threads of life together and sharpens our inner awareness of peace and well-being.

Turn on the background music and invite participants to sit back, close their eyes, relax as much as possible and prepare for a peaceful, healing journey.

Read slowly and expressively. Allow plenty of time for participants to form the images and enjoy the sensations.

&&&

Allow yourself to relax as much as possible in your chair...
with your hands resting comfortably in your lap...
Uncross your legs and let your feet be flat on the floor...

Take in a deep breath...
and as you exhale...let your eyes close...
Continue to take slow...deep...easy breaths...

Think of each breath as cleansing you...
clean fresh air coming in like a cool drink...
And each time you exhale...let your tensions flow with the current of air out of your body...

Think only about your breathing...
and let anything else on your mind flow out with your breath...

Feel yourself relaxing...
as each breath removes the tensions and worries of your day...

Feel the weight of your hands in your lap...

and imagine them floating as if on clouds...
There is no tension in your arms...
as they are floating lightly with your hands...

Your shoulders settle down as your muscles relax...
and your head may drop slightly down and forward...

With each breath, you become even more relaxed and at ease...

You may become aware of your heart beating smoothly and rhythmically...
You can feel the blood pulsing through your body...
to your legs and feet... to your arms and fingers...
flowing to every cell... bringing the oxygen of your breath...

Feel each breath flowing deeply into your body...
bringing life to every part...

The blood also carries the nutrients from your last meal...
What you have eaten has been absorbed...
and now this nourishment flows to rebuild and strengthen your body...
Energy is delivered to every cell and stored for ready use...

Imagine your body using that energy...
moving with ease and grace...

Think back to a time when you enjoyed some playful movement... carefree and fun...
Remember the buoyant feeling of freedom... and how good you felt...

Continue to ride these feelings...moving freely...
and passing through time to another place...
a favorite place where you feel safe, calm and content...

It may be a garden or a meadow...
a secluded shore or under the brilliant night sky...
wherever is your favorite place...

You can feel the peace and tranquillity of this special
place... You feel like you belong here...
You are at peace with yourself and your world...

And as you think of the beauty and specialness of your
favorite place...
you realize the miracle of its creation...and your own...

There is peace within you now...
as you tune in to yourself and your Creator...
knowing the joy of this life-giving connection...

Now it's time to start coming back to this room...
to the present place and time...
But you can bring the peace with you...
and make it an ever-present part of your life...
As you nurture yourself and others with wholesome
food...
as you enjoy the spirit of play...
as you experience the acceptance of one another...
and the love of the Creator...this peace will remain
with you...

And if you should lose this feeling of peace...
you know you can come back and find it any time...
just the way you did here...for it is always present
within you...

Open your eyes when you are ready... and go in
peace...

Submitted by Grant Christopher.

Adapted from *Structured Exercises in Wellness Promotion, vol. 4.*

$\mathcal{J}$ust for Today

This memorable meditation based on twelve-step programs challenges participants to tackle positive changes in their lives one day at a time.

Time
5–10 minutes

Introduce the script by reminding participants that most of us have agendas for change that are overwhelming and unrealistic. Suggest that the best way to tackle change is one step at a time, one day at a time.

Be sure to tell them that Abigail Van Buren, the source of this script, adapted it for her annual New Years column from the traditional AA credo.

&&&

Just for today, I will live through this day only and not set far-reaching goals to try to overcome all my problems at once. I know I can do something for twelve hours that would appall me if I felt that I had to keep it up for a lifetime...

Just for today, I will be happy. Abraham Lincoln said, "Most folks are about as happy as they make up their minds to be." He was right. I will not dwell on thoughts that depress me. I will chase them out of my mind and replace them with happy thoughts...

Just for today, I will adjust myself to what is. I will face reality. I will change those things that I can change and accept those things I cannot change...

Just for today, I will improve my mind. I will not be a mental loafer. I will force myself to read something that requires effort, thought, and concentration...

Just for today, I will do something positive to improve my health. If I'm a smoker, I'll make an honest effort to cut down. If I'm overweight, I'll eat nothing I know is fattening. And I will force myself to exercise — even if it's only walking around the block or using the stairs instead of the elevator...

Just for today, I will be totally honest. If someone asks me something I don't know, I will not bluff: I'll simply say, "I don't know"...

Just for today, I'll do something I've been putting off for a long time. I'll finally write that letter, make that phone call, clean that closet, or straighten out those dresser drawers...

Just for today, before I speak I will ask myself, "Is it true? Is it kind?" And if the answer to either of those questions is negative, I won't say it...

Just for today, I will make a conscious effort to be

agreeable. I will look as good as I can, dress becomingly, talk softly, act courageously, and not interrupt when someone else is talking...

Just for today, I'll not improve anybody except myself...

Just for today, I will have a program. I may not follow it exactly, but I will have it, thereby saving myself from two pests: hurry and indecision...

Just for today, I will have a quiet half hour to relax alone. During this time I will reflect on my behavior and get a better perspective on my life...

Just for today, I will be unafraid. I will gather the courage to do what is right and take the responsibility for my own actions. I will expect nothing from the world, but I will realize that as I give to the world, the world will give to me...

Adapted from *Structured Exercises in Wellness Promotion, vol. 5.*

$\mathcal{M}$ealtime Meditation

In this relaxing sensory meditation, participants tune into ways to nurture themselves at mealtime.

Time
10–15 minutes

This process is most effective just before a meal or refreshment break. Begin with a warm-up talk on mealtime as an opportunity for self-care.

Hunger is our internal call for nourishment. Our bodies signal us when we need food or water. When we care for ourselves, we listen to these physical cues and respond accordingly.

Listening to our bodies is sometimes difficult. We are bombarded by external cues to eat: tempting food ads; business meetings scheduled at noon; family and friends gathering to socialize and celebrate; fast food lanes offering convenient, inexpensive food; and vending machines with snacks everywhere.

We often eat for non-physical reasons including habit, scheduled meals, eating to prevent hunger later in the day, and dependence on the advice of authorities about what, when, and how much to eat.

Encourage participants to relax and then begin the script.

☙☙☙

Take a moment now to relax...
Settle back in a comfortable chair...
and allow your body to rest against the surface of the chair...

Take a deep breath...close your eyes...
and fill yourself with air...
Then let it out...slowly and easily...
blowing softly out of your mouth...
Breathe in again...deeply through your nose...
filling your lungs from bottom to top...
Then slowly...softly...let that breath go...
relaxing and calming your body...

Pause 5 seconds.

Continue to breathe deeply...slowly and easily...
responding to your body's call for air...
Filling the exact needs of your body with each breath...
Not too much...not too little...
Each breath brings the perfect amount...

Pause 5 seconds.

Imagine your body's need for food...
and your response to this call...
It's easy and natural...like breathing...
responding to your hunger...
giving your body the nourishment it needs...

Not too much... not too little...
but just the right amount for you...

Notice the rhythm of your breathing...
as you consider your need for food at this very
moment...
Focus on the feelings in your body...
as you allow yourself to listen to hunger signals...
which may be vibrating from your abdomen...
softly stirring, rumbling, or roaring...

Notice these sounds and sensations...
Listen to the voice of your body...

Pause 5 seconds.

Perhaps it is quiet... satisfied... resting...

Images of non-physical hungers may drift in and out of
your awareness...

You might find your thoughts drifting off...
to a pleasant fantasy... or distractions from your day...
If this happens... simply notice these thoughts and
sensations...
as you let them pass through your awareness...
Whatever you are doing... wherever you are going...
whatever you are feeling...
is exactly right for you at this moment...
You are wise... and your body is wise...

You can trust yourself to know what to do for
yourself...
and how to do it...
You are your body's best friend...

Notice the sensations in your mouth...
Tune in to the kind of food that your mouth wants to taste...

Pause 5 seconds.

Does it crave a soft, creamy food...or a hard and crunchy texture?
Does it want something hot...or cold...liquid...or solid?

Perhaps images of food will pass through your mind...
Allow them to move through your awareness...simply noticing them...
You can trust yourself to make wise choices...
knowing how to feed your body what it needs...
to stay healthy...active...and feeling good...

You can trust your body to tell you what it needs...
and you can trust yourself to satisfy these needs...

Pause 10 seconds.

As you continue to relax and explore your hunger...
you are aware of your human needs...
and you accept and love yourself...
You are worthwhile...
and you deserve the life-sustaining nutrients of a good meal...

Let yourself have exactly what you want...and the pleasure of eating it...
Food is not your only pleasure...
so you can relax and enjoy your meal fully...
trusting that you will not overeat...

You can give yourself exactly what you need...
no more... no less...
Eating is like breathing... natural and easy...
You will stop when you have had enough...

Focus now on the kind of food you are wanting...
and the amount that you think you need...
Pay attention to these ideas and images...
and trust yourself to use them wisely...

Pause 10 seconds.

As you prepare to return to the present...
know that you can take this knowledge with you...
when you go for your next meal...

You can continue this feeling of relaxation...
and confidence in yourself... and your body...
You are your own best friend.

When you are ready...
slowly open your eyes... and return to the present...
feeling relaxed... calm...
and connected to your body...

Adapted from *Structured Exercises in Wellness Promotion, vol. 5,*
available on the CD and audiotape *Eating.*

Massage for Tension Relief

$\mathcal{P}$ushing My Buttons Self-Acupressure

In this unusual self-care technique, participants stimulate several acupressure points to get their energy flowing again.

Time
10–15 minutes

Invite participants to join you in a healthy, energizing break based on self-acupressure techniques interpreted from ancient writings found on the walls of the Shaolin Temple in China. Be sure to experiment with the process and find your own pressure points before trying to explain them to the group.

You will be massaging specific areas of your body, including many pressure points, where the body's energy flow can be stimulated.

You will discover the exact location of your pressure points by noticing the spots that feel different or a little tender. Steady pressure or gentle massage should relieve the pain and release the energy.

Ask people to follow along as you talk the group through the 13 steps, describing and demonstrating the various strokes that are used for the different pressure points.

1. Rub the top of your head briskly with both palms.

2. Use both thumbs to locate the depression at the base of your skull in back, where it meets the spine. Starting in the middle and moving out toward the sides, staying just below the bony (occipital) ridge, locate pressure points about one inch apart all across the base of the skull.

   Most people have several tender spots in this area, so don't hurry—use enough pressure with your thumbs to feel the tenderness at each spot, but not enough pressure to create acute pain. After a few seconds this press can be released or expanded into a gentle circular massage.

3. Rub your nose vigorously, kneading, pulling and moving it around. Try a two-handed noserub!

4. Massage the lobe of each ear between your thumb and index finger. Make sure the whole perimeter gets a thorough rubdown, then pull gently. Finally, cup your hands over your ears and give the whole area a quick up and down rub.

5. Use your thumbs to trace along and beneath your lower jaw. Use moderate pressure and move very slowly. Start in the corners under the ears and follow the jaw bone to the midline, thumbs meeting under your chin.

6. Using the fingers of your right hand, rub across your chest from the left shoulder to the sternum, staying below the line of the collarbone. Hold your fingers like a curved garden rake and make strong back-and-forth movements, kneading the muscles as you slowly move across your chest. Repeat on the left side using the right hand.

7. Flex your left arm. Use your right thumb to locate the pressure point in the crook of your elbow, just outside the bone of your lower arm. Feel around, using a fair amount of pressure until you find the trigger point. Hold and release. Repeat for the right elbow.

8. Use the thumb and one finger of your right hand to circle your left wrist. Hold your hand steady and quickly rotate your left arm in a screwing motion so that the left wrist gets a vigorous massage. Repeat for the right wrist.

9. Make fists with both hands. Now reach back and gently pound the kidney area with your fists. At this angle you should get just enough pressure for stimulation.

10. Using both hands in a rhythmic motion, clap and slap both thighs up and down and front and back, as far as you can reach and as long as it feels good.

11. Move down to the area of your kneecap. Using short back-and-forth strokes with your fingertips, knead the entire area above, around and below the kneecap, extending down to massage the protrusions below and outside of the kneecap. If

you find any tender spots, stop, apply more
pressure and release.

12. Run your thumb along the inside of your shin to a
point about 4 fingers above the ankle bone. When
you find the tender spot, use a thumb press for
several seconds, release and then repeat. Be sure to
stimulate the pressure point on both legs.

Pregnant women should not stimulate this point.

13. Use whatever strokes feel good and spend as much
time as possible massaging your feet. Try thumb
circles, kneading, pulling, clapping, rubbing—on
the top, bottom, sides, edges, between the toes,
along the arch, etc. If the room is carpeted, try
rubbing the soles of your feet vigorously on the
floor.

Submitted by Jackie Mosier.

Adapted from *Structured Exercises in Stress Management, vol. 3,*
available on the CD and audiotape *Massage.*

Revitalize Your Eyes

Using an ancient self-care technique, participants practice acupressure techniques for relieving tension and eyestrain.

Time
2–5 minutes for each technique

Introduce the ancient technique and benefits of fingertip acupressure.

Our eyes are natural tension collectors: they are always on the job adjusting to external environments (lighting, airborne irritants, temperature) and taxing activities (reading fine print, video monitors, rapidly changing focus.) We rarely give our eyes a break, except during sleep.

Acupressure has been used for centuries in the Orient to relax the focusing muscles of the eyes and to increase blood circulation. Many schools and factories provide time twice a day for these simple but effective self-care routines.

Rubbing around the eye socket affects a number of acupressure points that aid in relaxation.

Describe and demonstrate each step of the acupressure self-massage, inviting participants to follow along.

&‑&‑&

Gently close your eyes and relax as much as possible.

Take a deep breath and allow your mind to clear.

Draw your attention inward and let your eyes relax by visualizing the color black.

Now use your thumbs or middle fingers to massage the pressure point along the ridge of your eye socket,  underneath your eyebrow, at the inner corner of your eye.

You'll recognize the pressure point by a sense of tenderness, or even a slight pulsing.

Use a rocking and rolling massage motion, rubbing toward the nose, then away again.

Massage rhythmically to a count of eight. Rest. Then repeat the eight-count massage five or six more times.

Don't forget to keep breathing deeply.

The second pressure points to massage are on either side of the bridge of the nose, about where your glasses might rest.

Find the tender/pulse spot and grasp it with your thumb and finger.

Massage by squeezing up and down to the eight-count. Rest. Repeat five or six more times.

The third set of pressure points are along the lower ridge of the eye socket, below the midpoint of your eye.

Use your middle fingers to massage these points. You can brace your thumbs on your jaw for better leverage.

Rock and roll massage for the eight-count. Rest. Repeat.

Continue to relax as you finish this exercise. And when you are ready, open your eyes and let them continue to relax by gazing out the window or across the room.

Submitted by Larry Tobin.

Adapted from *Structured Exercises in Stress Management, vol. 4,* available on the CD and audiotape *Massage.*

Fingertip Face Massage

In this gentle self-care exercise, participants experience the relaxing, revitalizing power of touch.

Time
10–15 minutes

Invite participants to join in a special treat — a nurturing self-care technique that can be used whenever relaxation, refreshment, or revitalization is needed.

&&&

You've decided to be special to yourself... to give yourself something you need... a nurturing touch... a chance for you to become... comfortable... relaxed... and revitalized in just a few moments...

Please move into as relaxed a position as possible while remaining seated... If you're wearing glasses... you may want to take them off now...

I'd like you to begin by rubbing your hands together... Get your hands just as warm as you can... and feel the energy in your hands... Continue to rub your hands together... and when they become all nice and warm...

and are feeling good...I'd like you to close your eyes...
and to place your hands on your face.

You may find yourself covering your eyes to block out
the light...Do whatever is comfortable for you...and
simply hold the palms of your hands on your face for
awhile...Feel their warmth on your face...and feel
those sensations of tenderness that come with holding
your face...

And now, with your fingers, begin to gently massage your
face...Move your fingers gently and comfortably across
your forehead...allowing your fingers to relax the lines in
your forehead...and to soothe them...Give your
forehead the kind stroking and attention it would like...

That may be a gentle touch...a soft touch...or it may
be a harder touch...one with more pressure...
Whatever motion or touch you choose...enjoy the
activity...and give yourself a chance to allow your
fingers to relax...and comfort your forehead...

And now...move down slowly over the other areas of
your face...gently massaging and caressing...the area
of your eyes...Feel your hands and fingers over your
eyes...and now your cheeks...and your nose...

Pay attention to what your face may be saying to you...
Pay attention to what it needs and wants from you...
Listen to what feels good...and enjoy that...And then
move on to other parts of your face...

Continue moving down your face...and across your
lips...and chin...and jaw...Feel your fingertips and
your hands...as they massage the lower part of your

face...And feel your breath on your hands...when your hands move across your mouth...And enjoy the sensations you have...with the warmth of your breath...and the warmth of your touch...

Now that your face has become more relaxed...and comfortable...and you've given yourself a chance to be as tender with your face as you can...I'd like you to experiment with a new way of touching your face...

This time...use your fingertips to stimulate your face... by tapping it...gently...across your forehead...across your temples...and cheeks...and over your nose...Feel the energy that comes as you tap...Feel your fingertips dance on your face...enjoy that stimulation...

And then let your fingertips dance on your head... vigorously or slowly...whatever comes naturally to you...As your fingers dance...imagine that you're giving your face and your head new life...you're giving it new stimulation...And enjoy the feeling of stimulation...enjoy the new life.

As you're doing this...allow your eyes to begin to feel a glow...to feel a kind of waking up and sparkle...Feel that sense of sparkle and vitality all throughout your face...In your eyes...on your cheeks...even in your nose...your lips...and your mouth...

Give yourself pleasant, warm thoughts...joyful thoughts...And take a deep breath...as you feel yourself once again...through your breathing...

Now...place your hands on your face...as you say good-bye...for now...Allow your face to say thank you... to your hands... for giving it this special care and attention...

You've filled yourself now... with something that you may need... And this is something you can do for yourself anytime of the day... Whenever your face... your body... your mind... or your spirit... need some nurturing... some new stimulation...

Adapted from *Structured Exercises in Wellness Promotion, vol. 2,* available on the CD and audiotape *Massage.*

Weather Report

In pairs, participants simulate meteorological phenomena as they exchange back rubs. In the process, they release muscular tension in neck, shoulders, and back and learn to enhance relaxation through imagery.

Time
5–10 minutes for each partner

Invite participants to pair up with a neighbor for a revitalizing meteorological experiment. As soon as everyone has a partner, instruct the pairs to decide who is a winter and who is a summer.

Be sure everyone has a partner. If there is an uneven number in the group, you get to participate too.

Instruct the summer person in each pair to sit down in a chair and the winter person to stand behind and place hands on summer's shoulders.

As soon as everyone is in position, guide the winters in massaging the head, neck, and shoulders of their summer partners, using the images and instructions in the Weather Report script to describe the process.

Demonstrate the techniques as you describe them.
Encourage receiving partners to give feedback with
appreciative sighs, groans, and exclamations — and to
report any discomfort. Givers adjust their technique
accordingly.

Snowflakes

Begin by tapping your fingers lightly along your
partner's shoulders. Gradually extend these gently falling
snowflakes up the back of your partner's neck and then
to the top of the head.

Raindrops

Now move back to the shoulders and turn those
snowflakes into raindrops tapping a little harder across
the shoulders, up the neck and all over the scalp.

Hailstones

Return again to the shoulders and pretend your fingers
are hailstones, cascading down out of the sky. Flick your
wrists and tap harder all over the shoulder, head and
neck area.

Thunder

Now use the thunder stroke massaging the same area.
Cup your hands and clap them across the shoulders and
down along the top of the arms.

Lightning

Next comes the lightning. Use the sides of your hands
and a chopping motion to pound the large muscles of the
shoulders and upper back. Try different intensities. Check
with your partner to find out what pressure feels good.

Tornado

Massage the whole neck and shoulder area with thumbs. Press deep into the muscle and rub in circles that resemble the eye of a tornado.

Meteor Shower

Now make fists and pound down the back on either side of the column. Adjust the intensity of this meteor shower to your partner's liking.

Tidal Wave

Return now to the starting position for the tidal wave. Place your palms on top of your partner's shoulders and use the heel of your hand to move the muscles of the shoulders back and forth like kneading bread.

Partners exchange positions and Step 2 is repeated, with the trainer guiding summers through the massage of their winter partners.

Submitted by Martha Belknap

Adapted from *Structured Exercises in Wellness Promotion, vol. 3.*

*T*reats for Tired Eyes

In this revitalizing self-care break, participants practice four techniques for relieving tension and strain in an often-neglected body part. These strategies reduce eyestrain and tension, and learning them also provides a relaxation break.

Time
1–2 minutes for each technique

Introduce the exercise by mentioning some of the sources of eyestrain: many hours in front of a computer, lots of reading, fluorescent lighting, air pollution, and allergies.

&&&

Breathe and Blink
We'll begin with the simplest tichnique, which is great for the eyes — a healthy dose of oxygen.

Breathe deeply and blink your eyes several times. This technique increases blood flow and brings additional oxygen to the eyes.

Try it again now — and several more times later in the session.

Warm Bath

When your eyes get tired, your whole body feels tired. This "bath" will revialize tired eyes.

Begin by rubbing your palms together until they are warm.

Close your eyes and cover them completely with your warmed palms. Relax. Open your eyes in the darkness.

Breathe deeply several times while cradling your head in your hands.

Close your eyes again, and lift your head.

Now exhale forcefully, releasing all remaining tension while you slowly open your eyes again.

Eyeball Calisthenics

The eye, like any other body part, benefits from deliberate exercise to strengthen muscles and reduce tension. Try these eyeball calisthenics that can be done several times a day.

Close your eyes if you wish, and cup them in your palms. Relax in this position as much as possible.

Now move your eyeballs as far to the right as possible. Then far to the left. Now up and down as far as you can stretch.

Now roll your eyes around clockwise.

For maximum benefit, each of these routines should be repeated 5–10 times in each direction.

Black as Night
Now it's time to give your eyes a well-deserved rest.

Close your eyes and cup them in your palms.

Visualize "black" as though you were in a dark room with your eyes open.

Let any points of distraction dissolve into blackness.

Relax and enjoy the vision of total darkness.

Remind participants to try these revitalizing breaks several times a day for tension prevention and for headache relief.

Submitted by Larry Tobin.

Adapted from *Structured Exercises in Wellness Promotion, vol. 5,* available on the *Massage* CD and audiotape.

Stretching Routines

$\mathcal{E}$ight-Minute Stress Break

Participants learn a 14-step stretch routine that stretches all the major muscle groups. This quick and easy routine can be used as a stress break any time of the day.

Time
10 minutes

Introduce stretching and exercise as effective preventive measures for dealing with stress by systematically letting go of tension before it accumulates to unhealthy proportions.

&&&

1. The 360 Stretch
Begin with your body relaxed, arms and hands loose at your sides. Pull your right shoulder up and with one smooth movement, bring the shoulder back and around, making a complete circle.

Repeat this same circular motion with the left shoulder.

Continue stretching one shoulder, then the other, five times each. Then reverse the direction, using alternate shoulders, five times each.

This should loosen up your neck, back and shoulders—places where most people store tension.

2. Snow Angels

Allow your arms to hang loose at your sides. Begin to loosen your wrists by shaking your hands, allowing them to flop as freely as possible.

Continue to shake and flop as you slowly raise your arms to the side and up until your hands touch overhead.

Then allow your arms to gradually drop, still shaking and loosening the wrists.

3. Bunny Hop

Put your hands on your hips and hop twice on your right foot. Now hop twice on your left foot.

Continue these double hops, alternating feet and adding a side kick or a cross kick on the second hop.

Continue hopping and kicking for 30 seconds, varying your tempo and kick height.

4. Cloud Walk

This is a slow step, rolling from heel to toe, one foot at a time, gently stretching the legs and feet. Your whole body should be relaxed.

Pick up the tempo of the heel-toe roll until you reach a slow jog, raising your feet slightly off the floor at each step.

Continue at this pace for 30 seconds.

5. Starfish Stretch

Begin with your arms stretched overhead, slightly bent, eyes turned upward.

In a single motion, open your hands, spread your fingers wide, and reach up as high as you can. Hold that position for a few seconds. Then close your fists and lower your arms, with elbows bent.

Rest a few seconds and then repeat the starfish stretch/ rest sequence 10–15 times.

For variety, stretch to the side.

6. Tall Grass Stalk

Extend your arms out in front of you.

While concentrating on your shoulders, slowly sweep your hands and arms to the side and back, as if pushing tall grass out of the way.

You should feel a pull along your shoulders and arms. Stretch your arms out again and "stalk" for ten more steps.

7. Hoe-Down

Start by getting centered, feet firmly planted, knees slightly bent.

Lift your right knee up towards your chest, slap it with your left hand and then lower your leg and stretch it to the side, toes pointing outward.

Repeat the hoe-down lift 3 more times and then try the left leg for 4 counts.

8. Dippity-Do

Start with your legs slightly apart.

Dip your body into an easy kneebend and then spring back to the upright position.

Continue to bend and spring back for 30 seconds, adding rhythmic arm swings as you increase your pace.

9. Arch Stretch

With knees slightly bent, join your hands comfortably behind your back.

Slowly arch your back, letting your hands and stiff arms pull your shoulders and head down toward the floor.

Hold for 5 counts and then relax, allowing your head to fall forward and your shoulders to curl toward the front.

Repeat 7 times.

10. Body Bounce

With feet apart, arms at your sides, bend sideways at the waist, stretching your hand down your leg as you straighten up.

Repeat the stretch and bounce to the other side. Do five body bounces on each side.

Now add your arms to the stretching movement. With your left arm, reach up and over as you bounce to the left 3 counts.

Do 5 sets on each side.

11. The Wave

Stand straight with your arms at your sides, palms facing out.

As you take a long deep breath, slowly (4 counts) raise your arms up over your head. Now, as you exhale slowly, bring your arms back down, palms facing downward (4 counts).

Repeat this languid wave 6 times.

12. Twister

With feet shoulder width apart and knees bent, put your hands on your hips.

Keep your back straight as you twist your shoulders and trunk to the right 3 times and then return to face forward.

Now twist to the opposite side for 3 counts and return to the center.

Continue to twist for 8 sets.

13. Sneak Peek

Stand straight with your neck, shoulders, and back as relaxed as possible.

Tilt your head to the left. Now slowly roll your head so that your chin falls to your chest and then comes up as your head tilts to the right. Now look back over your right shoulder, hold the pose and then relax.

Repeat the stretch, this time starting with your head tilted to the right and ending with a sneak peek over your left shoulder.

Do four peeks on each side.

14. Hang Loose

Time to shake out your body.

Flap your arms, twist your wrists,
shrug your shoulders, jiggle your legs, shake your feet,
flex your knees.

Bounce your booty until your whole body feels tingly,
loose and relaxed.

Submitted by Keith Sehnert, MD.

Adapted from *Structured Exercises in Stress Management, vol. 3.*

C*louds to Sunshine*

This adaptation of a traditional T'ai Chi exercise allows participants to breathe and stretch easily and to focus and let go of mental distractions while imagining four different scenes from nature.

Time
3–5 minutes, may be repeated several times

Invite participants to stand and join in a revitalizing stretch based upon traditional T'ai Chi movements. Demonstrate as you read the instructions.

&&&

Clouds
Stand with your knees relaxed and your hands cupped in front of your pelvis.

Inhale and draw energy up from the earth through your body.

Invert your hands and push the clouds toward the sky.

Rain
Exhale and lower your arms in an arc down to your
sides.

Allow the rain to fall gently upon the earth.

Rainbow
Clasp your hands together behind your back and lift
your arms as you inhale.

Exhale and bend forward with your arms extended
behind you.

Form a rainbow with your body over the land.
Inhale and lift. Relax arms to sides and exhale.

Sunshine
Turn your palms upward and lift your arms in an arc
overhead as you inhale.

Exhale and embrace the sunshine with your arms
making a circle in front of your chest.

Inhale and draw the sunshine into your heart.
Exhale and feel the sun bathe your body.

Adapted from *Structured Exercises in Stress Management, vol. 3.*

$\mathcal{G}$*iraffe*

In this pleasurable visualization, participants learn a
simple stretch routine for relaxing the neck and
shoulders.

Time
5 minutes

*Explain that stress-related tension in the shoulders and neck
is a common side effect of desk jobs and a frequent cause of
fatigue and headaches. Invite participants to join in a
stimple stretch designed to relieve tension in those areas.*

&·&·&

Sit in a relaxed, erect position...
Take a deep breath and let it out with a big whoosh...
Take another deep breath and let your body relax as
much as possible...

As you are doing this exercise, pay attention to the
stretching and opening you may feel in your neck...

Slowly let your head and trunk roll forward...
Bring your head lower and lower...
stretching your entire spine from top to bottom...

When you reach the lowest point, rest there for a
moment...
Now slowly bring yourself erect again...
vertebra by vertebra...as if you are stacking the building
blocks of your body one on top of the other...
Keep your chin tucked in until you are almost
completely erect...

Finally, bring your chin and head up...
As you make this final movement...
imagine that your head is being pulled up by a string...
attached to the top from the sky above you...

Feel the long stretch in your neck muscles...
and be aware of your head...
effortlessly floating free above your neck...

Imagine that like a giraffe in the jungle you have
an immensely long and graceful neck...
that allows you to stretch above the treetops...

Look around up there...
and enjoy the pleasant sensations of stretching...
and floating...for as long as you care to...
Then slowly let yourself return to normal proportions...

Adapted from *Structured Exercises in Stress Management, vol. 4.*

Tension Tamers

From this collection of stretches for all parts of the body, choose one or two appropriate for your group and then lead participants in an energy-restoring, relaxing stretch break.

Time
2–3 minutes

&&&

Yawn and Sigh

Ask participants to stand and participate in the yawn and sigh routine.

Take a big yawn or two—opening your mouth and throat until the automatic yawn response takes over.

Demonstrate the yawn as you describe it, exaggerating the sound effects and motion dramatically. Encourage people to make noise as they yawn.

Now it's time to sigh. Take a quiet inhale and then make a long noisy exhale that relaxes your throat and chest muscles. Practice several noisy sighs.

Overcome inhibitions by cajoling people into noisier and noisier sighs. Exaggeration helps people let go.

Lead the group in a sequence of yawn and sigh combinations.

Stretch

Instruct participants to stand and stretch

Arch your back, stretch your arms and fingers out wide, holding that position 5–10 seconds — and then to let go, allowing your body to go completely limp.

Repeat this stretch 2 or 3 times.

Sedentary Stretch

Give instructions for a simple stretch participants can use to relieve muscle tension from static postures.

Sit up straight. Bring your shoulders back as if you're trying to touch your shoulder blades together. Hold that position for 7–8 seconds and then release.

Next, curl your shoulders forward, as if trying to touch them in front. Hold for 7–8 seconds and then release.

Repeat this stretch 2 or 3 times.

Triple Shake

Ask participants stand with their arms hanging loosely at their sides.

Shake your fingers, hands, wrists, and arms on up to your shoulders. Continue shaking until your arms feel warm and tingly. (10–20 seconds)

Direct participants to use the same shaking procedure on their legs, one at a time. (10–20 seconds)

Finally, ask participants to shake their trunk and whole body.

Tender Loving Touch

Demonstrate the Tender Loving Touch technique and then lead the group through the process.

Rub your hands together briskly until they are warm.

Now, close your eyes and lightly cup your hands over your eyes, with fingertips resting gently on your forehead, thumbs along the temples, the heels of your hands on your cheeks.

Maintain this position for 2–3 minutes, letting go of all the tension in your eyes and face, and allowing yourself to truly relax.

Submitted by Mary O'Brien Sippel

Adapted from *Structured Exercises in Wellness Promotion, vol. 1.*

$\mathcal{G}$ood Morning World Stretches

This sequence of gentle Yoga stretches and rhythmic breathing will release muscle tension and activate mind/body energy as participants learn to center themselves.

Time
3–5 minutes

Play soft, flowing music without a distinct beat as a background to this script.

Give instructions and demonstrate the breathing/stretch routines as outlined below, asking participants to pay particular attention to coordinating their breathing with the movement.

After participants have learned the sequence, encourage them to continue the stretch for several minutes, moving at their individual pace. Remind them to listen to their bodies and stretch gently.

&·&·&

The Salute

Step	Breathe	Movement
1	IN	Stand with arms at side (this is "center")
2	OUT	Palms together in front of chest, elbows bent (prayer pose)
3	IN	Link thumbs, raise arms above head, arch back
4	OUT	Thumbs linked, bend forward at waist, reach toward floor
5	IN	Stand, repeat #3 (arms above head, arch back)
6	OUT	Repeat #2 (prayer pose)
7	IN	Return to "center" (rest, arms at sides)
8	OUT	Rest

The Pump

Step	Breathe	Movement
1	IN	Stand with hands clasped behind seat ("center")
2	OUT	Palms together in front of chest, elbows bent (prayer pose)
3	IN	Link thumbs, raise arms above head, arch back
4	OUT	Thumbs linked, bend forward at waist, reach toward floor
5	IN	Stand, repeat #3 (arms above head, arch back)
6	OUT	Repeat #2 (prayer pose)
7	IN	Return to "center" (rest, arms at sides)
8	OUT	Rest

The Airplane

Step	Breathe	Movement
1	IN	Stand and raise arms to sides with right palm up and left palm down ("center")
2	OUT	Bend to the left keeping arms outstretched
3	IN	Return to "center" and reverse palms, left palm up, right palm down
4	OUT	Bend to the right, keeping arms outstretched
5	IN	Return to "center" (arms out)
6	OUT	Lower arms to sides
7	IN	Rest with arms at sides
8	OUT	Rest

Adapted from *Structured Exercises in Wellness Promotion, vol. 2,* available on the *Yoga* CD and audiotape.

As the Seasons Turn

In this series of gentle Yoga stretches, participants use images of nature to help them relax, releasing tension through conscious breathing and movement.

Time
5 minutes

To support the slow, rhythmic breathing and movements, you may want to use quiet background music with an even tempo, such as Pachelbel's "Canon in D."

Demonstrate the movements and guide participants through the cycle of seasons several times.

&&&

Spring
Stand with knees relaxed and your hands resting in front of your pelvis.

Imagine a strong oak tree with its roots reaching deep into the earth in springtime.

Inhale as you draw up nutrients from the soil—up through the trunk of the tree, out to reach all the branches rising toward the sun as you raise your arms overhead.

Summer
With your arms stretched overhead,

Imagine the tree at its peak of fullness in the middle of summer.

Exhale as you extend the branches to the side stretching your arms wide to the side at shoulder height.

Inhale as you reach the branches upward again raising your arms.

Autumn
Make your tree very tall, with your thumbs linked overhead,

Imagine the west winds of autumn.

Exhale as the tree bends to one side.

Inhale and lift to center.

Exhale as the tree bends to the other side.

Inhale and lift to center.

Exhale as the leaves are blown to the ground and you drop your hands to your sides.

Winter
Clasp your hands behind your seat,

Imagine the branches of the tree laden with fresh snow in winter.

Inhale as you lift your arms behind you.

Exhale as the tree bends forward, lowering its branches toward the ground.

Inhale and lift to the center position, then relax your arms.

Submited by Martha Belknap.

Adapted from *Structured Exercises in Wellness Promotion, vol. 4.*

Cobra

This gentle Yoga movements tretches the back muscles, expands the chest, and stimulates the inner organs. encouraging flexibility, reducing tension, and releasing trapped energy.

Time
5 minutes

This stretch is not appropriate for formal settings or after a meal. Loose, informal clothing and an empty stomach are best. Mats are required for comfort.

Invite participants to spread around the room and find a comfortable place to lie down for the cobra pause. Remind them that this should be a gentle stretch.

&&&

This Yoga posture is called Bhujangasana or the cobra.

Begin by lying down on your stomach...
with your forehead resting on the mat... arms at your sides...
Allow your body to ease into the pose...
Allow your body to relax as much as possible...

let the tension flow out of your muscles as you relax.

**

Now bring your hands up and place them between your
shoulders...
with palms flat on the floor and fingertips touching
under your chin...
Keep your elbows comfortably close to your rib cage...
Bring your legs and ankles together and point your toes.

To begin your stretch, imagine that you are in a super
slow motion video.
Very slowly raise your head...
feeling each vertebra slowly move as you allow your neck
to arch...
Ease into this stretch...don't push...
Hold it for 5 seconds.

Now, continuing in super slow motion, begin to raise
your chest...
pushing against the floor with your hands for support...
Again, ease into this stretch very slowly and don't
push...
Allow yourself to relax for 5 seconds.

Now, staying in super slow motion...
continue to raise your trunk off the floor...
allowing your spine to arch gracefully and easily...
vertebra by vertebra...
Your head should be arched back...your eyes looking
upward...
elbows slightly bent...spine arched...legs relaxed...
Hold this pose for a count of 10.

Now once again in super slow motion...
reverse your movement and lower your trunk...chest...
and head...
until you are back to the original position...
relaxing deeply with your forehead on the floor...
and your arms alongside your body ... ...sletting your
body go completely limp.

Close your eyes and rest for a moment.

And now repeat the sequence.

*Begin the script again at the **. Remind people to move
slowly, without jerking, relying on back muscles to lift and
arm muscles to support.*

Adapted from *Structured Exercises in Wellness Promotion, vol. 1,*
available on the *Yoga* CD and audiotape.

About Whole Person Associates

Whole Person Associates provides stress management, wellness promotion, and workplace productivity materials that actively involve participants and offer a "whole person" focus on body, mind, spirit, relationships, and lifestyle.

Counselors, trainers, therapists, educators, consultants, and group leaders use our resources, which include:

- Books of structured exercises on many topics, which are adaptable to different issues, age groups, learning styles, and life experiences
- Video courses on stress, healthy living, and workplace relationships
- Relaxation audio and video
- Self-help books
- Biofeedback equipment and popular Biodots
- Health promotion materials
- Resources for parents and teachers
- Ready-to-Run workshops
- Assessment tools

Call 800-247-6789 to request a catalog, or view or products and order online at www.wholeperson.com.

Printed in the United States
55136LVS00006B/397-480